This book is beautifully written.
stand the Epistle of Galatians in
tive. The way Johannes W. H. van der Bijl brought the Acts into
this commentary in the narrative form is so clever. Through a
rich and beautiful narrative, this book brings us closer to Paul's
world and straight into the struggles of the early church, in such
a way that we feel part of the team that Paul and Barnabas led.
This book is easy to read but also has solid theological depth.
It brings the powerful message of Paul's letter to the Galatians
to light and shows us how it is still relevant today.

**Dwi Maria Handayani, PhD**
Program Director, Bandung Theological Seminary, Indonesia
Director, Langham Preaching Asia and South Pacific

It is truly a delight to read through the narrative commentary of Johannes W. H. van der Bijl's on the Pauline Epistle to
the Galatians. Storytelling is welcome in gatherings across age
groups. This is especially needed to rediscover the beauty of the
oral cultures of the Majority World.

The beginning of this narrative opens to the backdrop of
Paul and Barnabas, talking to each other over the sad news
of their Galatian converts being urged by the Jewish believers
to submit to Jewish religious customs and practices – already
encapturing the reader's full attention. The writer not only en-
gages the reader's mind and understanding in building up each
specific plot, but also structures the content to align with the
historical facts and happenings of the first century Christian
world.

This work is creatively done, making the Epistle of Galatians
sound out loudly and lively. It will spark the interest of younger

readers, who may be thirsting for truth that can be seen and touched. Paul, himself, should be glad to see this narration, as he once said: "God has put us . . . on display . . . We have been made a spectacle to the whole universe, to angels as well as to human beings." (1 Corinthians 4:9) I highly endorse this work to all readers.

**Rosa C. Shao, PhD**
Author and Clinical Psychologist
Faculty, Global Mission Seminary, California, USA

# GALATIANS

## A LIFE IN LETTERS

Langham
GLOBAL LIBRARY

# Galatians

*A Life in Letters*

Johannes W. H. van der Bijl

Langham
GLOBAL LIBRARY

© 2024 Johannes W. H. van der Bijl

Published 2024 by Langham Global Library
*An imprint of Langham Publishing*
www.langhampublishing.org

Langham Publishing and its imprints are a ministry of Langham Partnership

Langham Partnership
PO Box 296, Carlisle, Cumbria, CA3 9WZ, UK
www.langham.org

ISBNs:
978-1-83973-920-0 Print
978-1-83973-940-8 ePub
978-1-83973-941-5 PDF

All Scripture translations in this work are the author's own.

**British Library Cataloguing-in-Publication Data**
A catalogue record for this book is available from the British Library

ISBN: 978-1-83973-920-0

Cover & Book Design: projectluz.com

# Contents

# Foreword

For nearly ten years I have taught courses in New Testament Survey to groups of about twenty-five university students. Time after time I witnessed their enthusiastic engagement with the Gospels and the book of Acts, only to see their interest dwindle in the second half of the course, when coming to the Epistles. In the culture of the Middle East, as in many other cultures, many prefer to do theology through narrative rather than discursive text and are drawn to the first half of the New Testament.

Yet, there is narrative in and behind the Epistles. They are not collections of abstractions but communication from person to person, community to community. Historical critical scholarship has gone a long way in recovering the narratives in and behind the Epistles, but students can easily lose their way in the technical and discursive language of scholarly commentaries. We need commentaries that take us into the narrative of the Pauline communities and, indeed, the narrative of Paul and his co-authors.

Johannes van der Bijl's narrative commentary on the Epistle to the Galatians does exactly that. And as it narrates, it captivates and educates. It takes the reader to a house in ancient Antioch, where the apostle Paul, with other leaders of the church, might have written this letter. Through imaginative dialogues it brings out the apostle's deep concern for the spiritual wellbeing of the Galatian Christians, whose faith was threatened by a misapprehension of law and grace.

The narrative is informed by engagement with the Greek text and recent scholarship. It builds on the South Galatian hypothesis, favouring an early dating of the letter before the apostles' meeting in Jerusalem. The events of the first missionary journey, as told in Acts 13 and 14, guide the interpretation. We meet Paul, Barnabas, and the other leaders of the Antiochian church just before they travel to Jerusalem to discuss the requirements for new believers from among the Gentiles. The nature of Christian freedom is at stake. Van der Bijl shows how this was a personal concern for both the authors and the recipients of this letter.

The medium of story organically evokes the Jewish and Graeco-Roman contexts. Smells, sounds, and sights enable the reader to imagine the process of reflection that lay behind this letter. We see Paul pacing around the room and dictating sentences. We listen to heated conversations about the thorny issues that the Galatians faced. We feel the joy of the breakthrough of an insight.

Readers should remember that this is a commentary on, and not a rewriting of, the Epistle to the Galatians. Van der Bijl is, in many ways, pioneering a new genre in biblical commentary. His approach is to reconstruct the possible and probable circumstances surrounding the writing of the letter and the conception of its theological content. Just like other commentaries, it is an approximation and interpretation, this time in the form of a narrative. It should be read as critically as other commentaries.

If so used, this commentary is eminently suited as a first introduction to Paul and the letter to the Galatians. It may serve as a textbook in courses on Pauline literature and prove its value as an inspirational aid in the preparation of sermons and Bible lessons. In cultures that appreciate storytelling, this is a welcome new approach in biblical studies.

**Wilbert van Saane**

Haigazian University and the Near East School of Theology,
Beirut, Lebanon

# Preface

While Peter is certainly the most developed disciple in the Gospels, Paul undoubtedly shares the title in the Acts of the Apostles and surpasses Peter in the Epistles. Perhaps this is why there is so much more written about Paul than there is about Peter!

And this, of course, begs the question: Why write yet another book on Paul? What do I have to say that would add to the collective knowledge of this towering figure? The answer is quite simple. Nothing. I have nothing to add. But I do have a different style to offer that might be helpful to those who learn primarily through narrative . . . through simple storytelling.

Of course, some may point out that Paul's letters were written in a propositional style, using logic and rhetoric, whereas a narrative style is more concrete, using stories and images to convey truth. But I would argue that Paul's letters are full of concrete stories and images, especially in his use of Old Testament quotations . . . quotations that would have conjured up the stories and images contained in the greater context of those quotations.[1] Besides, the real, tangible, flesh-and-blood person, together with other real, tangible, flesh-and-blood people who may have helped in the drafting of each letter – all grappling with real-life issues of cultural and religious plurality in a first-century world – cannot be removed from the letters.

This current volume – and, God willing, those volumes that will follow – seeks to examine, in part, the apostle Paul's

---

1. See Koehler, *Telling God's Stories*, 32–35, and Harvey, *Listening to the Text*.

story – his life and his theology – through the lens of his own letters, following an accepted chronological order. Each letter is set in the framework outlined for us by Luke in Acts and by Paul himself in his Epistles. While some speculation is inevitable when dealing with historical figures since, most often, not everything can be known about the character – for example, details about the person's childhood – I have tried to stay as close to the scriptural texts as possible. I have also endeavoured to stay true to the cultural practices of the day. As with all my books, these volumes are no substitute for the Scriptures; they are simply narrative commentaries.

It is my hope and prayer that my small contribution will bring glory to the one who is ultimately the hero of all our stories – God our Father, Jesus our Lord, and the Spirit, our life-giver and guide.

# Acknowledgements

I am grateful to all who have encouraged me in the writing of this first book in the narrative commentary series on Paul's life and labour as seen through the book of Acts, his own writings, the writings of others, as well as a few church traditions. Thanks especially to my wife, Louise, who so lovingly and patiently reads through the material, offering helpful suggestions here and there for improvement. Of all married men, I will always be the most blessed.

# Preamble

Acts 7:57–8:3; 9:1–31; 11:19–30

> Our story begins after the so-called First Missionary Journey. Paul and Barnabas had been in Antioch for a while when they receive bad news from the churches in Galatia, informing them that Jewish believers were attempting to persuade all Gentile converts to submit to Jewish religious practices and customs.

Paul held the open parchment before him, his hands trembling, his breathing shallow and rapid.

"But why are you so upset?" Barnabas asked. "Jesus taught that if they are not against us, they are for us and that we should not forbid them to . . ."[1]

"This is not a question of for or against, Barnabas," Paul interrupted. "This is a foreign gospel altogether. It is a fundamental betrayal of everything we believe and teach and practise. Never in the history of our people has deliverance come through the observance of any law! We obey the law because we *are* God's people, not the other way round. Ever since Adam's fall, it has always been God who seeks us out

---

1. Mark 9:38–41.

first[2] . . . no human being has ever sought after God.[3] He is found by those who do not seek him."[4]

Barnabas sighed as he sat down next to his colleague. In his opinion, it was unfortunate that Paul possessed the kind of emotionally passionate temperament that caused him to experience life a little more intensely than most people. This often resulted in spur-of-the-moment assessments and decisions that Paul later regretted – like what had happened with Barnabas's cousin, John Mark.

He took a deep breath and then said gently, "Well, I haven't read the letter from our Galatian brethren yet, so you will have to help me understand."

"Have you forgotten where I came from?" Paul shot back, his eyes still fixed on the parchment in his hands.

Barnabas hesitated. He was not sure he understood what Paul meant by this clipped statement. Paul often spoke in puzzling terms and, at times, was hard to understand.[5] While Paul knew exactly what he was trying to communicate because he knew what he was thinking, his listeners were often at a disadvantage as this knowledge was not mutual. Barnabas had learned that Paul's thoughts had to be teased out with probing questions until the speaker and the listener were together on the same level of understanding. For this same reason, Paul was not always the most eloquent speaker[6] – that they both agreed on – but he had a sharper and more perceptive mind than most people and the ability to think through highly complex

---

2. Genesis 3:8–9; see also Deuteronomy 7:7–11; John 6:44; 15:16; Acts 13:48; 1 John 4:19.

3. Psalm 53:1–3.

4. Isaiah 65:1.

5. 2 Peter 3:16.

6. 2 Corinthians 10:10; 11:6.

theological concepts and then distil these into clear drops of pure wisdom.

"I'm not sure I understand what Tarsus has to do with this letter from Galatia."

Paul looked up suddenly, as if he had been stung by a wasp. "Tarsus?"

"You asked if I had forgotten where you came from . . ."

"Barnabas!" Paul said, with a hint of exasperation, "I don't mean geographically."

Barnabas exhaled slowly. He gazed out over the city of Antioch. It was considered the third largest city in the world and, although it was a thriving Roman colony and home to many Syrians and Greeks, had a sizeable Jewish population. Situated on the banks of the River Orontes at the foot of Mount Silpius, it was often called Great Antioch.

Peter had first established the church at Antioch[7] after a number of converts had settled in the city following the great outpouring of the Holy Spirit on the day of Pentecost.[8] Then believers from Cyprus came and began to reach out to non-Jews, and so the church began to multiply across ethnic boundaries, with disciples making disciples who made more disciples.[9] This was the disciple-making method that Jesus had used with his followers and they, in turn, had continued to train others to do the same.[10]

---

7. This is according to Orthodox tradition: "Church tradition maintains that the See of Antioch was founded by Saint Peter the Apostle in A.D. 34." http://ww1.antiochian.org/patofant. See also: https://christianity.stackexchange.com/questions/68875/is-there-any-evidence-to-support-the-claim-that-the-apostle-st-peter-founded-th.

8. Acts 11:19.

9. Acts 11:20–21.

10. I explored this fourfold method of Jesus in my previous books, *Breakfast on the Beach* and *For the Life of the World*.

Since Peter had already left for Rome, Barnabas had been sent to investigate reports they heard from Jerusalem of ethnic inclusion.[11] Finding a growing, healthy community at Antioch, he then went to Tarsus to find Paul – who, at that time, was known as Saul – and the two of them laboured long and hard to build up the increasingly vibrant church in Antioch that now served as their base for further mission work in Asia.[12]

The believers in the city were so well taught and led that they closely resembled Jesus in their speech and behaviour. Previously believers had simply referred to themselves as followers of the Way.[13] But now, the local people scoffed and called them "Christians" – meaning "little Christs."[14] Sadly, anti-Jewish conflicts broke out in the city after zealous Jews strongly resisted Emperor Caligula's attempt to erect a statue of himself in the temple in Jerusalem.[15] But still, the church there continued to thrive, perhaps because of its mixed membership.

Paul was a good choice for such a multi-ethnic community. He was excellent at reasoning with both the Jews and the Hellenists.[16] It was as if he had so immersed himself in the Scriptures that when he spoke, every sentence was impregnated with allusions or direct quotations. He was also well versed in Greek writings and philosophies. But his intelligence often caused him to assume that others understood his line of reasoning when, in fact, they did not.

"You mean your background in *Judaism*?" Barnabas ventured.

---

11. Acts 11:22–24.

12. Acts 11:25–26.

13. Isaiah 40:3; John 14:6.

14. Acts 11:26.

15. See Philo Judaeus, *On the Embassy to Gaius*, 30.203.

16. Acts 9:22, 29; 18:28; 19:8–10.

"Yes, of course," Paul replied, clearly trying hard to suppress his irritation. Now he, too, lifted his head to stare vacantly at the city lying sprawled out before them. Mount Silpius dominated the skyline and caused Paul to remember the comforting words of a psalm: "I look up to the hills and wonder: what is the source of my help? Surely it is the Lord who made heaven and earth."[17] His breathing slowed down as he allowed his mind to take him back in time to his old family home.

---

17. Psalm 121:1–2.

# 1

# Childhood[1]

Acts 16:37; 18:3; 22:3–29; 23:6; Romans 9:3–4;
2 Corinthians 11:22; Philippians 3:5–6; 1 Timothy 1:15

> Paul revisits his formative years as a son of a
> Pharisee and a student of Pharisees to explain why
> the news from Galatia disturbs him so much.

My ancestors were Pharisees,[2] and my parents were strict, devout observers of the law – not just the Torah, mind you, but the pronouncements of the rabbis and the sages, too, the so-called oral law. Every part of my childhood was governed by rules and regulations. We lived in the hope of the Coming One . . . the one spoken of by the prophet Malachi . . . the one who would suddenly come to his temple in all his glory to ratify the covenant . . . the one who would return to purify the Levites

---

1. As very little is known of Paul's childhood – except where he came from, that his ancestors were Pharisees, and that he had a sister living in Jerusalem – this chapter is mostly speculation on my part.

2. Acts 23:6.

like a refiner's fire.[3] A hope that would surely only be fulfilled when we ceased to do the things for which we were sent into exile in the first place. We had to keep the law! Otherwise, we would remain under the yoke of the pagan nations."

"Our ancestors lived in this hope even through the darkest periods of our history," Barnabas said, contemplatively. "From the time of Abraham, we were always looking for the fulfilment of what God had promised."[4]

"But my father believed that that hope had to be actualized. That hope had to be reflected in everything we said and did and thought and prayed. We had to live it, breathe it, sleep it, eat it, wear it. Our lives were lived in constant devotion to God. We had to be zealous for his law. Nothing could be left to circumstance or chance. We had to be pure . . . holy, even as our God is holy. Our very lives and our very identity depended on it. And so, my father made sure that every itinerant preacher who passed through the town stayed with us. Our meals were punctuated by long deliberations and debates. I must confess that, at first, I found this tedious. I would much rather have been playing outside with my friends. But I soon realized that any sign of interest from me . . . any indication of comprehension . . . any hint of a desire to participate in the discussions, would please my father immensely. So, I stayed, I listened, I learned; and then, one day, I spoke."

Paul rose to get himself a cup of water. He leaned against a pillar, still staring out over the city. Then he turned and looked at Barnabas.

"You know, I will never forget the look on my father's face when I first engaged our visitors." He laughed. "Actually, I'll

---

3. Malachi 3:1–3.

4. Genesis 12:1–3.

never forget the look on our visitors' faces either. I was a mere child . . . only eight years old. What did I know of the law? But that did not stop me from quoting the Scriptures I had learned, along with the interpretations of the rabbis I had listened to at previous discussions! You see, I had committed to memory all their contrary arguments."

Paul smiled as he remembered. "My father's face shone like the sun at midday. He was so proud."

He sighed as he returned to sit down once more. "My mother was not allowed to be present in the same room with us, of course, but she was listening from the other side of the wall. We could never hide anything from her! There was a glow about her the next day . . . a glow that would brighten even more whenever she looked at me."

Paul paused and then added, "It was that night that sealed my fate."

"Sealed your fate?"

"Yes. That group of rabbis returned to Jerusalem and spoke of nothing else but this wonder child they had met in Tarsus. A few months later, my father received an invitation for me to go to Jerusalem to study under the great Gamaliel."[5]

"You were only eight when you left your parents?"

"No," Paul chuckled. "No, my mother would not hear of it! She might not have been allowed to be in the same room as the men, but she still had the final say about her children – that is, my sister and I."[6]

"So, when did you go?"

---

5. Acts 22:3. See also https://readingacts.com/2011/09/07.

6. Acts 23:16.

"Four years later. You see, Ima[7] wanted me to come of age in Jerusalem, and she wanted to be there with me for the occasion. I think, at first, the delay frustrated my father, but he soon learned how not to let this postponement get in the way of my advancement! To make sure I excelled in my learning in the meantime, he bought every scroll he could afford and engaged the very best scholars as my tutors. Soon I was spending more time in the synagogue than at home! He wanted to make sure I was a Hebrew of Hebrews, zealous and blameless with regard to the law!"[8]

"But it was also your father who made you learn the Greek writings, is that not what you told me?"

"Yes, the philosophers . . . the pagan sages.[9] Of course, I did not read them all, but what I lacked, I picked up from simply listening to our Gentile neighbours and customers."

"Was that helpful, do you think? Did that not confuse you? Did it not muddy the pure waters of Judaism?"

"Oh, no! No, they were immensely helpful! Not for building up my faith as such but for strengthening my resolve to know what I believed and why. Studying their philosophies helped me understand why those outside of Israel do what they do. And this came in handy later, after I had come to believe that the hope of Israel had been fulfilled in Jesus. It helped me explain, to both Jews and Gentiles, how what we thought was a localized and nationalized deity with a localized, nationalized promise actually had a global presence and a global plan. All

---

7. *Ima* is a Hebrew word for "mother."

8. Philippians 3:5–6; 2 Corinthians 11:22; Romans 9:4; 11:1.

9. "The people of Tarsus have devoted themselves so eagerly – not only to philosophy, but also to the whole round of education in general – that they have surpassed Athens, Alexandria, and other schools of philosophy." Strabo, quoted in Walker, *In the Steps*, 34.

that study helped me to speak with them about matters of the faith. Knowing what others believe and why they believe helps you understand their behaviour and their manner of thinking. It helps you formulate your approach when engaging them, whether in debate or in defence. As you know, the pagans are at once inquisitive and challenging. So, you use their words, their so-called wisdom, their poems, their stories – stories they know well and can relate to – so that when you reason with them about things they do not know, you are able to address them in a way that they can understand."

"It doesn't sound as if you had much time for anything but study . . . what about your friends?"

Paul gazed down at the mat before them. He traced the weave of the flattened reeds with his fingers. "Sadly, I hardly saw any of them, and when I did, it was as if there was a great gulf fixed between us."

He paused momentarily, as if reflecting on the lost joys of childhood. Then, looking up from the floor, he drew in a sharp breath and said dismissively, "But later they became less important to me than my studies. Besides, we had very little to talk about since many of them had stopped their lessons and were engaged in their fathers' trades."

"But like Jesus and the other rabbis, you also learned a trade . . ."

"Tentmaking, yes.[10] Not my primary focus those days but a helpful trade, nonetheless. It made my father a very wealthy man . . . a man who could buy his Roman citizenship."[11]

---

10. Acts 18:3. For a helpful discussion on trades see: https://www.blueletterbible.org/Comm/edersheim_alfred/sketches/sketches11.cfm.

11. See Bandy, *Illustrated Guide*, 20–22, for a different take on Paul's Roman citizenship . . . as a token of the triumphant Octavian's appreciation for their support of him during his war against Cassius and Brutus (42 BC). We

"Yes, I remember you telling me that . . . That was how you came to be born a Roman, not so?"[12]

"Yes. My father bought his citizenship so that his children would be born citizens. Don't get me wrong, learning his trade was good. It is a profitable craft and one I use now, as you well know, to finance what we do but one that I did not appreciate at the time. You see, I wanted to learn, to excel, to know more than every teacher I had ever met. Studying the law became my controlling passion. I wanted to surpass my instructors and outshine them all. I knew my father would be so pleased!"

Paul clapped his hands together loudly, startling a few birds and waking up a dozing rooster that immediately began to crow.

"His little boy . . . all grown up to be a scholar . . . the first in the family. I was intent on making him proud. But I must say that I have since realized that this tentmaking trade was one of the best things I learned during that time."

"And then you went to Jerusalem?"

"And then I went, yes," Paul replied. "There, I came of age, and my parents were so happy. For them, it was a dream come true. My father spared no expense. I was a man – and not just any man! I was a scholar – and not just any scholar but a pupil of the great Gamaliel! Ah, I was so full of myself."

He stopped speaking abruptly, then said softly, as if to himself, "Pride so often parades itself as humility, does it not?"

Paul sighed. "It pains me to think that at the very time I assumed I was so holy and so scripturally based, I was really

---

know from Paul's statements in Acts (see below) that he received citizenship because he was born into a family that had Roman citizenship. Early Church theologian and historian, Jerome, thought that Paul's parents were brought to Tarsus as prisoners of war from the region of Gischala in Judea.

12. Acts 16:37; 22:25–29.

the worst sinner of all.[13] God scorns the proud; it is the humble who please him.[14] But all I saw then was how great I was, how special, how gifted, how blessed. I was so self-assured."

He paused, then added, "But I must admit, Barnabas, I was a little scared when my parents left me behind in the city. I felt like a little lost lamb for a time, but I soon learned to deal with my anxieties and my homesickness through the rigorous discipline of plunging myself deeper and deeper into further study."

"But you did not adopt the more moderate way of your teacher, did you?"

"No." Paul groaned and buried his face in his hands. "No, to my shame I must confess that in my zeal to purify Israel, I wanted to follow the example of Phineas,[15] Joshua,[16] David,[17] Elijah,[18] and Mattathias,[19] and I sought to purge Judaism of this new sect by capturing, torturing, hounding and slaughtering the followers of the Way, as they called themselves at the time."

Paul smothered a sob with a cough. Then, with his eyes burning like coals of fire and with a bitter tone of anguish in his voice, he said, "And *that* is why I am so angry with what these Jewish believers[20] have done in Galatia." Paul rapped his knuckles on the floor. "They have opened the door to a bottomless pit of self-righteousness and an impossible life of

---

13. 1 Timothy 1:15.

14. Proverbs 3:34; James 4:6; 1 Peter 5:5–6.

15. Numbers 25:6–9.

16. Joshua 8:26–29.

17. 1 Chronicles 28:3.

18. 1 Kings 18:40.

19. 1 Maccabees 2:49–64.

20. The false teachers were Jewish believers, like those mentioned in Acts 15:1 and Acts 15:5.

striving for redemption through merit when, in truth, salvation is a free gift from God through Jesus."

"So, what are you going to do about this?"

"Me? I am going to write them a letter . . ."

# 2

## Preparation

Acts 13:1–13

As they prepare to write a letter to the confused and
bewildered Galatian churches, Paul and Barnabas
share reflections of their First Missionary Journey.
Their strong disagreement with regard to John
Mark's sudden return to Jerusalem from Perga
causes Barnabas to suggest that they write the letter
together with their trusted companions in Antioch.

D o you remember what it was like," Paul asked, checking
the nib of a quill with his fingers, "this trip for which we
were set apart?"

"Yes, I do," Barnabas replied thoughtfully. "How could I
forget? You were gravely ill as we pushed our way up through
those mountains. And then, later, you were nearly killed."

"No, I was thinking of even before that," Paul said, flattening
out a few rolls of parchment with his hands. "I was thinking of
our calling and our commissioning in Antioch and then our

9

trip to Cyprus. That was a first for me. Do you remember that sense of anticipation, Barnabas?"

"Yes, I remember." Barnabas paused for a moment and then added, "My cousin was still with us then."

Paul's eyes darkened for a moment, but he chose not to say anything about John Mark's departure from Perga.[1] He was still angry about what, to him, was nothing less than a desertion and an abandonment of God's mission. How dare the young man question his methods? Paul believed that Mark had decided to return home to his mother because Paul and Barnabas had not demanded that Sergius Paulus be circumcised – in line with the usual requirements for Gentiles seeking to convert to Judaism – and then, he assumed, once Mark arrived back home in Jerusalem, he had told the brethren there about what Paul and Barnabas were doing.[2] Paul had also assumed that it was because of Mark that some in the community who used to belong to the stricter sect of the Shammaites[3] in Jerusalem decided to send their representatives to Galatia. To Paul, John Mark was a traitor to the cause.

"Our trip to Cyprus," continued Paul, picking up where he had left off instead of speaking what was on his mind, "was so new and invigorating. Such a small but beautiful island, with

---

1. See Acts 13:13 on Mark's departure. See Valdez, *On the Shores of Perga*, 56–59, for a well-reasoned discussion on the meaning of the word *apochōreō* – which is variously translated as "deserted," "separated," "departed," or simply "left." Valdez (and Deissmann) argues that the fact that Luke exclusively uses John's Hebrew name here indicates that it was a theological objection that caused the rift.

2. See Stott, *Message of Acts*, 221, and Longenecker, *Acts of the Apostles*, 421.

3. Rabbi Shammai, the founder of the more conservative group within the sect of the Pharisees, insisted on converts keeping the whole law, being circumcised, undergoing ritual cleansing, keeping the Sabbath, complying with dietary restrictions and so on.

its forests and mountains. But also such a strategic location for trade. No wonder no empire could ever leave it alone! And that is why it was good place for us to start our mission. Mark my words, our teaching will travel further with every ship that docks there."

Barnabas responded enthusiastically to Paul's positive assessment. "I think the whole trip was so invigorating, but I was especially moved by our being appointed for the work God had called us to do. You know, I remember that as if it were yesterday. The command was so clear. The Holy Spirit spoke so directly, but we still wanted to make sure. It was all so new and so foreign . . . to be guided by God's Spirit in this way, I mean."

"Yes, to be led by the Spirit is incredible. And we are also blessed to have a wonderfully supportive spiritual family here in Antioch, aren't we? They are so open to the guidance and direction of the Holy Spirit."

"Yes, indeed. I think, for me, it was not just the initial call of the Holy Spirit for us to be set apart for this task of taking the gospel to the West but also the commitment of the community here in the laying on of their hands and their sending us out . . . commissioning us, as you said."

"Yes, that helped when the going got tough."

"It did," Barnabas agreed. "That and the fact that we started out in familiar territory . . . well, at least familiar for me."

"You know, it still makes me smile to think that a Levite ended up in Cyprus."

Barnabas felt a wave of mild defensiveness wash over him. "Cyprus has a sizeable Jewish population. You saw how many synagogues there were in Salamis alone! We were not the only Jewish family living on the island."

"True . . . but you were living on the island while you and your family had land in Judea!"

"Oh, Paul! You and Peter! The expectations that Levites not own their own property faded with the restoration after the exile. You know that. Besides, I sold the land and gave the money to the community in Jerusalem."[4]

"I know, I know," Paul chuckled. "I'm only teasing you. But seriously, how providential that you still had family in Cyprus, so that we had somewhere comfortable to stay. It really did help to get us going on our very first journey as apostles!"

"Yes," Barnabas concurred, "and all did go well, didn't it? Especially in Paphos! You know, I can't help thinking that just a few years earlier, a Roman governor in Jerusalem sentenced Jesus to death, but there in Paphos, another Roman governor accepted him as his Lord and Saviour![5] The irony of it all! No wonder that false prophet, Bar-Jesus, wanted to prevent this from happening."

Paul made a hissing sound as he breathed in sharply through his teeth. "What a slimy and slippery character! I still shudder when I think of him. He was so like the serpent with Eve in the garden, blinding the proconsul to the truth of God's word. But he was judged accordingly. Blindness for blindness."

"You know," Barnabas said thoughtfully, "I still wonder if he did not curse you and if that was why you got so sick in Perga. You could hardly see by the time we reached Pisidian Antioch."[6]

"That is possible," said Paul, rubbing his chin thoughtfully. Then he added, almost defensively, "But I still maintain that we had to press on. We had no choice. That mountain pass would have been blocked with snow and, if we had not left

---

4. Acts 4:36–37.

5. Acts 13:12.

6. It is possible that Paul was struggling with an illness that affected his eyesight. See Galatians 4:13–15. See also Rendall, *Epistle to the Galatians*, 135–36.

immediately, we would have been forced to spend the winter in Perga. Besides, God used even that for good. If it wasn't for my infirmity and the harsh weather conditions, we would not have received such a warm welcome in Pisidian Antioch!"

"Fair enough," said Barnabas, nodding slowly. "And, also, we would not be writing this letter . . ."

Paul suddenly slammed his fist on the floor. "Oh, why did your cousin have to tell the brethren in Jerusalem about our mission?"[7]

Barnabas was somewhat perplexed by this unexpected outburst. "Would you have had Mark lie to them? Lie to his mother?"

"No, but he should have said nothing."

"How then would he have explained his return from Perga?"

"He should have been loyal," Paul growled.

"Loyal? To whom? To you? You, who shouted at him and belittled him simply because he dared to question your refusal to circumcise Sergius Paulus? You know, I truly believe that had you handled the situation differently, Mark might never have left us in the first place. Your angry outburst was not helpful."

"Barnabas!" Paul shouted, his face red and the veins in his neck bulging, "What you don't seem to understand is that it is because of him that those false shepherds came to foul up the

---

7. While this is pure speculation on my part, it may explain why Paul was so fiercely adamant that John Mark not accompany them on their second mission. Mark must have done something more than simply return home – perhaps something like innocently reporting on what the team had done in Cyprus. Granted, we do not know for sure whether the "missionaries" were from Jerusalem or elsewhere, but Moo says that those "who had come to Galatia probably claimed some relationship to the apostles in Jerusalem" because Paul appears to focus on his relationship with Jerusalem in Galatians 1:13–2:10. Moo, *Theology of Paul*, 56. Paul's comment about the present city of Jerusalem being "in slavery with her children" (Gal 4:21–31) also seems to support this view.

drinking water of our lambs![8] Because of him, we now have to write this letter to clear things up."

"You don't know that for certain," Barnabas raised his voice. "Besides, do you realize how many factions there are within our own community, Paul? Just because others do not see things as clearly as you do, that does not give you the right to judge them or reject them! Some of us do think like you do, true, but others are not convinced. Even some in Judaism are divided on this issue![9] Our own community in Jerusalem is deeply divided, but they seem to be able to work together on a certain level despite their different ways of thinking."

Barnabas used the back of his hand to wipe away drops of spittle that had run down his chin. "And as far as my cousin is concerned, let me ask you this. Do you consider yourself perfect? Do you consider yourself without fault? Do we not all make mistakes – if Mark's leaving even was a mistake – that we later regret? Besides, as you have already pointed out, is God not able to use even our frailty to bring about something good?"

Barnabas was pacing up and down the room now, breathing heavily, his face red. He stopped abruptly and turned to face his stunned colleague.

"And besides, perhaps it is high time we think through the implications of our mission to bring the Gentiles into what has been, up until very recently, a predominantly Jewish community. In the future, we may even find that Mark has done

---

8. Ezekiel 34:19.

9. "Consider Josephus' account of the two very different opinions about how the non-Jewish King Izates should proceed in the present age to worship God and express pious adherence to a Jewish (Judean) way of life, either by becoming circumcised or not. Contrary opinions were espoused by two different Jewish informants, Ananias and Eleazar, and, interestingly enough, with a Diaspora setting during Paul's period (Ant. 20.17–96)." Nanos, *Reading Paul*, 19.

us a favour and that he has actually helped us with our ministry. He has opened a door we must walk through sooner or later by alerting us to a problem we must address if we are to remain a unified body of believers, Jew and Gentile together."[10]

Barnabas's mouth was dry, and his throat was sore. He was surprised at himself. He disliked confrontation intensely and usually avoided it if he possibly could, choosing, rather, to give a soft and gentle answer to those who were contentious.[11] Apparently Paul was equally surprised at the strong challenge for he said nothing.

For a moment, there was an awkward silence. Then Barnabas took a deep breath and quietly said, "You know, Paul, I think we ought to call the others before we put quill to parchment."

"What?" Paul looked up startled, as if he had been lost in thought.

"I said, I think we should call the others so that they can help us draft this letter."[12]

Paul sighed. He knew that his hot-headed and reckless nature often disturbed his partner.

"Forgive my anger, Barnabas. Perhaps it would be better not to speak about what is past. What is done is done, and it cannot be undone. Let us, rather, deal with the matter at hand."

"So, should I call the others?" Barnabas persisted.

"Yes. Yes, I think that is an excellent idea. That will give the letter a wider base of authority. Otherwise, they will say it was just my interpretation versus theirs."

---

10. See 2 Timothy 4:11, where it is clear that Paul had changed his mind about John Mark.

11. Proverbs 15:1.

12. Galatians 1:2.

"And," Barnabas added purposefully, "dare I say, it will also curb your temper."

Paul winced visibly. Yes, he was zealous for the gospel, perhaps as zealous for the gospel as he had once been for the law. It was good to have men like Barnabas to bring balance into his life.

"Thank you, Barnabas. I really do appreciate you . . . and your patient tactfulness."

"Well, then," Barnabas replied rather coolly, still smarting from the recent altercation, "I will find them, and once we are all assembled, then we will begin. Why don't you get a few things together for refreshments? I think this will be a long night."

"We have a few things in the house," Paul began, but then, seeing the expression on his partner's face, added, "Then again, I could go to the market quickly and buy something fresh. The walk might do me some good . . . help to clear my mind. Yes, I think I will do that."

"I will meet you back here within the hour."

"Perfect."

# 3

# Prologue

Galatians 1:1–5

> After being joined by other leaders of the
> church in Antioch, Paul and Barnabas explain
> to them the situation in Galatia and the need
> to address it in writing. Together, the group
> begin to draft a letter that will be copied
> and sent to the churches in Galatia.

I think we ought to pray and ask the Holy Spirit's guidance before we write a single word," Paul told the assembled group.

This small band of brothers, who had been the first prophets and teachers of the community in Antioch, still met together regularly for prayer, fellowship, and mutual encouragement. There was Simeon, whom they had nicknamed Niger,[1] Lucius,

---

1. Acts 13:1; Niger means "black" in Latin, likely because of the color of Niger's skin, which some have thought could mean that he was a freed slave from Africa. It would not be appropriate to nickname someone by their color today in many contexts, but here the nickname serves to highlight the rich diversity of the leadership of the church at Antioch, which had a member of

who was also originally from North Africa, and Manaen, who had been brought up with Herod Antipas. So their little group comprised a former slave, a tradesman, an aristocrat, a Levite, as well as a one-time Pharisee. Paul always joked that they were as diverse as Jesus's first followers.

"Niger, would you ask the Spirit to guide us as we write this letter?" Paul asked.

Niger cleared his throat. He stretched out his arms expectantly, as if waiting for a gift to be placed in them. The other men did the same.

"Oh, Sovereign Lord, we give you thanks that, in your mercy, you have rescued us for a purpose. You have restored us to our proper place in your kingdom so that we might be witnesses to you in all the earth. Endless is your compassion. Great is your faithfulness. We thank you, Lord, for the gift you have given us in the person of your Spirit, who is present with us here to guide us in your truth. He is the breath that renews us, body and spirit, and he gives us the very words we are to speak in this time of need. May we be renewed with faith in you, and may we be given wisdom as we seek to redirect your people in Galatia. Blessed are you, Lord God, King of the universe, fill us now with your wisdom as we wait on you. From your mouth, Lord God, comes knowledge and understanding.[2] Refresh our hearts and direct our thoughts so that in all we think and say and do, we might display the mind of Christ. Amen."

"Amen, come Lord Jesus," they said in unison.

For a while, they just stood in silence, listening in the stillness of the evening for that inner compulsion which they had come to know so well.

---

Herod's court, a Levite from Cyprus, a North African and a Black African. Every tribe, every nation, every tongue has a place in the kingdom of God.

2. Proverbs 2:6.

Lucius began to chant a psalm. "To you, O Lord, I lift up my prayer."

"In you, O Lord, we trust," the others joined in. "Rescue us from humiliating defeat, do not allow the enemy to triumph over us. Defeat is not for those who trust in you but for those who are rebellious. Teach us your ways, O Lord, cause them to be made known to us."

Their deep voices filled the room, Niger providing a rich harmony, and, as they sang, they sensed the warm glow of the Spirit. It was as if a light began to shine in them . . . a light that would bring clarity.

"May we be preserved by goodness and honesty because we place our trust in you. Save us, your people Israel, from all our strife and struggle."[3]

Once more they stood waiting in silence. It was Barnabas who eventually broke the quiet. "My dear brothers, I think by now you all know what it is that we need to do this night. Our brother Paul feels very strongly about this, as do I. So we want you to assist us in writing a letter to help the brethren in Galatia wrestle through this unfortunate and confusing teaching they have received from our Jewish brethren in the Way."

"This may seem insignificant to some of you, but to me it is like the breeze from the East, which, though gentle at first, alerts the fishermen on the Sea of Galilee to a coming storm," Paul said. "If ignored, it can be perilous."

"No Paul," Manaen interjected, "we do not think this is insignificant at all. We are all in agreement with you. We know that even a little false teaching can quickly spread throughout

---

3. See Psalm 25.

the whole area.[4] So, we must address this quickly and in the strongest terms."

"Should I be the scribe, Paul?" Niger asked. "You may struggle with your eyes in this lamplight."

It was getting dark quickly now, and the light from the oil lamps in the room did not give off much light.

"That is most kind, thank you, Niger. I may just add a few lines at the end."

At this point, they all sat down. Niger assumed the position of a scribe, sitting cross-legged, with the parchment rolled out on a large flat writing board.

"Paul," Barnabas said, "you are well versed in letter writing. How should we begin?"

"Well, I think we must first establish my authority as an apostle. They need to know, firstly, that my apostleship is not derived from our community here in Antioch[5] and, secondly, that it was bestowed upon me through the agency of Ananias.[6] I want to make it very clear that, just like the other apostles, my apostleship is also by divine appointment and that I was chosen for this task by none other than Jesus himself[7] and God the Father, who raised him from the dead."

"Good," murmured Niger as he wrote, "that will deal with any false ideas regarding your calling and your authority."

"I also think we need to add that this is not just a letter from me," Paul continued, "but, rather, a letter from all the brethren here at the church that sent us to them in the first place."

---

4. 1 Corinthians 5:6; Galatians 5:9.

5. Acts 13:1–4a.

6. Acts 9:10–19.

7. Acts 9:3–19.

"Yes," Barnabas agreed, "it will give the letter a little more weight if they realize that this is not just Paul's thoughts. There is a strength in harmony."

"To the church in Galatia?" Niger inquired.

"Churches," Barnabas corrected. "There are several churches in Galatia. This will be a circular letter, written to all of them in their respective cities and towns."

"To the churches in Galatia," Niger spoke as he wrote.

"Now," Paul said, "I also want to state my theological position clearly in these opening lines. We can expound on this as we go on."

"And that is?" Niger asked, quill poised in mid-air.

"It is what we believe . . . the true gospel – that God alone has taken the gracious initiative in establishing peace between us and him . . . that he has rescued us . . . that he has reconciled us to himself through the substitutionary sacrifice of Jesus."[8]

"In other words, you are saying that we cannot rescue ourselves, that our salvation is not something we can earn or gain by our own ability or by our following rites and rituals?" Lucius queried.

Paul smiled. "Yes, Lucius, that is exactly what I mean. The law was never meant to be a means of salvation. It has always been a way of life for those who are already God's children. The gospel is all about Jesus giving us what we can never generate ourselves. The gospel is all about him liberating us from slavery to sin, never about reward. As the Scriptures plainly teach us, there is not one person in the world who never sins and who always does what is right."[9]

---

8. Isaiah 53:12.
9. Ecclesiastes 7:20.

"What I find so astounding," Barnabas interjected, "is that by the will of our Father God, we have been liberated from the devastating power of sin right now, even in this evil time."

"Glory to him forever and ever!" Manaen shouted.

With one voice, the group said, "Amen."

# 4

---

# A Distorted Gospel

Acts 9:1–30; Galatians 1:6–2:21

> As the group begin to draft the letter, they discuss –
> in typical rabbinic question-and-answer fashion –
> the danger of what has happened in Galatia. Should
> this seemingly innocuous distortion of the truth
> proceed unchallenged, the death and resurrection
> of Jesus would be rendered meaningless.

To be perfectly honest, brethren," Paul said solemnly, "in the light of this remarkable kindness of our God, what *I* find astounding is that our brethren in Galatia have turned their backs on him who has called them into relationship with himself through the grace of Christ . . . that they have transferred their allegiance to another gospel . . ."

"But Paul," Niger interrupted, "surely there is no other gospel but the gospel that we believe?"

"That is correct, there is no other gospel, but I wish to make a point here. They think that what they are embracing is the full gospel . . . that somehow, we left something out in our preaching, whereas, in fact, what they have turned to is a distortion or a perversion of the one and only truth. There can only be one truth, and that is what we taught them."

"In other words, you are saying that they are being led astray by our conservative Jewish brethren," Manaen said sadly.

"Tragically, yes. There are still some of my believing countrymen who think that the Gentiles must first submit to all the requirements of Jewish law before they can enter the kingdom of God, that they must first become like Jews and live like Jews before they can become followers of Jesus."

Niger snorted. "That is like telling me I must first shed my darker skin for your lighter skin!"

For a moment there was silence, and then everyone burst out laughing.

"That's a good analogy, Niger," Paul said, wiping the tears of laughter from his eyes. "But seriously now . . ." He waited for everyone to get over the unexpected hilarity. "Brothers, I feel very strongly about this. Our brethren in Galatia need to know that if anyone – even we ourselves or an angelic being from heaven itself – should preach anything other than what they initially heard and accepted, such a person will be placed under a curse."

"A curse!" Barnabas objected. "Paul, that is strong language."

"Is that not what God instructed us to do?" Paul replied. "You know the Scriptures, Barnabas. In fact, they also know the Scriptures, and I am sure they will understand. In the law, God told us to let those who lead our fellow believers astray be cursed, remember? In the second giving of the law, we read that if anyone seeks to lead our people astray to serve what is not true, we must place them under a curse.[1] So, what I said

---

1. See Deuteronomy 13:12–18 where in the old Greek translation of the Old Testament the Hebrew word for "you must destroy it completely" and

before, I will say again: if anyone preaches something contrary to what they heard from us, let them be cursed!"

Still Barnabas hesitated. The word "curse" was so harsh.

Paul inhaled loudly, then said in a clipped manner, "Barnabas, do you think I am seeking to please anyone but God alone? Seriously, if I was seeking the approval of fellow human beings, I would not be serving Christ today. I would have continued in my old way of life."

"That is true," Lucius said. "You know, it is only now beginning to dawn on me what a grave error has been committed by these men. If we allow their false teaching to continue to spread unhindered, it will place huge stumbling blocks in the way of the Gentiles. In the past, many who believed in the God of Israel stopped short of fully embracing Judaism because they were reluctant to observe some of the Jewish rituals."

"Exactly," Paul agreed. "That is why I said that what these Jewish believers have done in Galatia is like that easterly breeze that alerts fishermen to a coming storm. For this reason, our newborn disciples in Galatia need to know that the gospel we proclaimed to them – the gospel they received and believed – did not originate with any human being. I did not receive it from any human, nor was it taught to me by any human; the gospel they received from us came through divine revelation from Jesus Christ himself."

"Yes," Barnabas acquiesced, "that is important. But I think it is also important that you explain to them what you explained to me earlier today. You need to let them understand your own background in Judaism. That will help them realize that you are speaking from personal experience."

"They already know all about my past life, Barnabas. Remember? I told them about how I was so zealous in my

---

"condemned things" are translated by the Greek *anathema*, which is the same word that Paul uses in Galatians 1 for accursed.

Jewish faith that I violently attempted to destroy the church of God. Don't you recall my telling them that I outshone all my contemporaries, that I was more zealous for our traditions than all of them?"

"Yes, I do remember, but it wouldn't hurt to remind them." Barnabas insisted.

"Uhm, I reworded what you just said, Paul," Niger commented, "Is that alright with you?"

"Read it to me."

Niger read from what he had written. "You heard all about my past life in Judaism, remember? I told you that I viciously persecuted the church of God and tried my best to exterminate it. I outshone all my contemporaries because I was far more zealous for the traditions of our forebears than they were."

"Yes, that's fine," Paul agreed. "Repetition does reinforce the argument. So maybe I ought to say *this* again as well: I want them to know that when God, who had set me apart even from my mother's womb[2] and graciously called me to be his own, . . . they need to know that when he was pleased to reveal his Son in and through me so that I might make him known among the Gentiles, I did not consult other human beings. In fact, I didn't even go up to Jerusalem at that time to speak with those who had been apostles before me. Rather, I immediately went into seclusion in the wilderness of Arabia."[3]

---

2. Galatians 1:15. Compare Psalms 71:6; 139:13–16; Isaiah 44:24; 49:1; Jeremiah 1:5; Luke 1:15b. It is quite possible that Paul, in Galatians, alludes to these texts to emphasize a similar summoning from God to a particular prophetic task, namely, to be an apostle to the nations.

3. See: Wright, *Paul: A Biography*, 62–65. Wright speculates that Paul followed in the footsteps of Elijah, who went to Mount Sinai in Arabia and then returned to Damascus. See Galatians 4:25; compare 1 Kings 19:1–18; Romans 11:1–6.

"I find that comforting," Niger mused. "That a person can be called of God for a purpose even before being born . . . that is, without even being aware of it. It tells me that everything we are as believers and everything we are called to be and to do comes about by God's initiative, not ours. Left to ourselves, we are nothing and can do nothing – isn't that what Jesus said?[4] Our very steps are directed by the Lord![5] Salvation has very little to do with us . . . it is neither earned nor merited. Besides, as the Scriptures say, we can make as many plans as we please, but it is the Lord's purpose that will be established."[6]

"That is comforting, indeed," Manaen agreed.

Silence descended on the group as each one pondered these reassuring thoughts.

"How long did you stay in seclusion, Paul?" Lucius asked, breaking the stillness.

"It was three years before I returned to Damascus. Only then did I go up to Jerusalem to compare notes with Peter.[7] And during the fifteen days I stayed with him, I did not speak to any other apostle except James, our Lord's brother." Paul glanced around the room as if needing some word of affirmation. "Truly, before God, I testify that what I am saying is not a lie. Before anyone else in the churches of Judea met me, I left and went into the regions of Syria and Cilicia. All they knew was that the same person who had been hounding the church had now

---

4. John 15:4–5; see also John 5:19.

5. Psalm 37:23; Jeremiah 10:23.

6. Proverbs 19:21.

7. Paul uses both the Aramaic name "Cephas" (perhaps to emphasize Peter's Jewish roots) as well as the Greek name "Peter" interchangeably throughout the letter. For the sake of clarity, I have chosen to use only the name Peter.

accepted the faith he had once tried to wipe out. And they gave all the glory to God because of me."

"And I can testify to the fact that he only went back to Jerusalem with me fourteen years later," Barnabas added. "You all know about this . . . how, because of the revelation of God,[8] you sent the two of us to bring relief to our brethren in Jerusalem."[9]

"Uhm, I'm going to write this down in the first person, as if these are all Paul's words, if you don't mind Barnabas. It will be too confusing otherwise."

"You are right, Niger, and no, I don't mind."

"It is very important," Paul said, "to also mention at this point that we took Titus with us."

"Why is that important?" Manaen asked.

"Well, it is important because after I had revealed to the leaders of the church – in a private meeting with them, mind you – the gospel I was preaching to the Gentiles, just to make sure I was not in error, they did not insist that Titus be circumcised, even though they knew that he was a Greek."

"Hmm, yes, that is very significant, I agree," said Niger. "Because by not forcing him to be circumcised, they set a precedent for future converts."

---

8. Acts 11:27–30.

9. There are two opposing views regarding this visit, one being that it took place at the time of the Jerusalem Council as recorded in Acts 15:1–35, the other that it was the famine relief effort recorded in Acts 11:27–30. Despite the difficulty with the timeframe mentioned in Galatians 2:1, I have decided to go with the latter view for three reasons: 1) There is no mention, in Galatians, of the Jerusalem Council's decision nor of their letter that was meant to be circulated among the Gentile churches (see Acts 15:19–21), a fact that would have strengthened Paul's position considerably; 2) The meeting Paul speaks of in Galatians 2:2 was private, whereas the Council gathering involved more than just the leaders of the church in Jerusalem (Acts 15:4–12); and 3) Their going up to Jerusalem in response to a "revelation" corresponds well with the prophetic word of Agabus regarding the coming famine recorded in Acts 11:27–28.

"Precisely! And even after false believers slipped in to spy on the freedom that is ours in Christ Jesus, hoping to force us to accept their conservative views, we did not relent because we wanted the truth of the gospel to prevail for the sake of other converts. Not one of the so-called leaders of the church – or whatever they were, does not matter to me because God is impartial in all matters – none of them tried to change my understanding."

Paul paused for a moment to take a sip of water. "In fact, they recognized that I had been entrusted with the gospel for the uncircumcised, just as Peter had been entrusted with the gospel for the circumcised. They concurred that the same one who had made Peter an apostle to the Jews had made me an apostle to the Gentiles. What's more, James, Peter, and John – whom you know are acknowledged leaders of the church – accepted the grace that has been given to me and, consequently, agreed to work with us to reach both ethnic groups. Their only requirement was that we remember the poor, which we were both quite willing to do anyway."

"And, later," Manaen added, "there was that confrontation here between you and Peter. Perhaps you ought to say something about that, seeing that you have referenced him as a leader in the church."

"Yes," Paul said, looking slightly embarrassed. "I still need to talk to him about my ill-timed outburst."

"You mean you ought to have dealt with the situation at hand in a more private manner," Barnabas said. "Like Jesus taught us . . . to deal with the offense man to man before making anything public."[10]

"Yes, I should have," Paul admitted awkwardly. "And I am truly sorry for it, Barnabas."

---

10. Matthew 18:15–16.

"I have forgiven you, Paul. And you will be able to speak with Peter when you see him in Jerusalem at the gathering."[11]

"Uhm, I have not added any of what you just said to the letter," Niger said. "I really don't think it is relevant."

"Yes," Paul said quickly, "but I do think we need to say something about the unfortunate incident because it does speak to the truth of the matter . . . that even a leader like Peter is open to correction should they insinuate that the Gentiles need to observe the rituals and dietary restrictions of Judaism in order to be accepted into the church community."

"So, what should I write?" Niger asked. "That you openly opposed Peter when he came to Antioch?"

"Yes, I opposed him because he was at fault. Before the contingent from James arrived, he was eating with all of us, Gentiles included. But after they arrived, he withdrew and would only eat with those who observed the strict dietary laws because he was afraid of being criticized."

"I think," Barnabas said, eyeing Paul as he spoke, a faint hint of a smile dancing at the side of his mouth, "that it was more because he was trying to prevent the very confrontation that his actions inadvertently initiated." Barnabas paused and, since Paul did not contradict him, then added, "Be that as it may, I must hasten to add that it was not only Peter. Several of us played the hypocrite along with him, including me. And by doing so, we unwittingly cast a slur of uncleanness on those whom God had already declared clean through Jesus."[12]

---

11. The Jerusalem Council (recorded in Acts 15).

12. The last sentence of this is derived from Rendall's helpful explanation in Rendall, *Epistle to the Galatians*, 163: "They were not dealing straightforwardly with the truth in casting the slur of uncleanness on those whom God had cleansed in Christ."

"And," Paul continued, "when I saw that they were not behaving consistently with the truth of the gospel, I rebuked Peter publicly, as I have already mentioned."

"Can you remember what you said?" asked Niger, hastily scribbling down the last words.

"I said, 'If you, as an ethnic Jew, lives by God's faithfulness just like the Gentiles, why then would you pressure them at this point to become Jewish?'"

"What exactly did you mean when you said that Peter 'lives by God's faithfulness just like the Gentiles'?" Lucian asked.

"I meant that we who are ethnic Jews and not ethnic Gentiles know that no one can achieve perfect righteousness through conformity to all the Jewish rites and rituals but, rather, that our righteousness comes through the faithfulness of Jesus Christ.[13] And so we know that even we who are Jews are justified only because of his faithfulness. We know that salvation to life never comes about by observing laws because we know that no human being can ever be declared just by merit."[14]

"But Paul," Manaen interrupted, "if Jews must be justified through Christ and are, therefore, as much sinners as the Gentiles, then doesn't this doctrine of Christ encourage us to live without reference to God's law? Does Jesus then become the agent of lawlessness?"

"Not at all!" Paul said, perhaps a little too sharply. "But if – after having believed that all without exception are justified through Christ – I then attempt to re-establish the rule of law as a source of justification, especially laws that will divide

---

13. Much scholarly ink has been spilt in assessing how to best translate the phrase often translated "faith in Jesus Christ" which I have here translated "faithfulness of Jesus Christ" – see the appendix for my reasons for going with this latter option.

14. See Psalms 130:3–4; 143:2.

our community once again, I am back to where I started . . . a hopeless transgressor of a law that no one can ever hope to obey."

Paul saw the frowns on his colleagues' faces and realized that they did not understand his explanation.

"Well, let me explain it this way. Through the law, I died to the law so that I might live to God. You see, when Jesus was crucified, I was crucified with Him."

"But how?" Lucian inquired.

"Jesus died in our place, Lucian," Barnabas said solemnly. "So, in that sense, we died with him. As such, the penalty of the law has been satisfied."

"Do you mean like the ram that died in the place of Isaac?"[15] Niger asked, forgetting for a moment to write.

"Yes," Barnabas replied, "except this time, Jesus the Son *was* the sacrifice. He *was* the substitute. By law, *we* ought to have died, but he died for us."

"By law, do you mean the sentence received by our forebears in the garden of Eden?" Manaen asked, puzzled.

"Well, yes," Barnabas said, "and no. Yes, we are all subject to the curse of Adam and Eve's faithless disobedience. Since their sin, we who are their offspring are dead even though we live. As King David tells us, we were conceived in sin.[16] And as the seer once said, who can bring something clean out of something unclean?[17] So, we are all already dead, but this is not only because of their sin but because of our own sin as well. Every human being is spiritually dead because we cannot but violate God's will. That is our natural state. Cut off from our

---

15. Genesis 22:13.

16. Psalms 51:5; 58:3.

17. Job 14:4.

source of life, we are dead in our iniquities and sins. The perfect law of God, given to us through Moses, reveals this deadness in us and proves our inability to find life in that state of deadness. The law shows us that we need God to breathe life into us once more . . . to resurrect us, as Paul is saying, before we can live in obedience to his law."

"And so, Niger," Paul indicated that he wanted him to write what he was about to say, "through the obedient faithfulness of Jesus – through his death and resurrection[18] – I live. Because he lives, I live. Yet, it is no longer I who live. Rather, I live because Christ lives in me. What I mean to say is that this new life I now live, I live because of the faithfulness of the Son of God, who loved me enough to give himself up for me as a substitute."

Paul turned to face Manaen. "So, I hope you can see that I am not dismissing the grace of God because if we could earn our own righteousness through law observance – if the law was sufficient in and of itself – then the death of Christ is rendered meaningless."

"Forgive me," Niger said suddenly, standing up and stretching. "I have a cramp in my calf from sitting in this position for so long. Could we perhaps take a short break?"

"I think that's a good idea," Barnabas said. "Let's stretch our legs a bit and have something to eat. Paul bought some refreshments for us earlier today. It might help us to think more clearly."

"Or it might help to keep us awake," Manaen chuckled.

"Since when does eating help you to stay awake?" Niger teased.

---

18. Philippians 2:5–8.

# 5

---

# Ruminating[1]

Acts 13:13–52

Retiring for the moment to the rooftop, Paul
and Barnabas retell the story of the First
Missionary Journey. Paul gives his reasons for
going to Pisidian Antioch, and the group discuss
Paul's method of preaching the gospel.

"Would you care to share your thoughts, Paul?" asked
Manaen, as he joined Paul on the roof of the house.[2]
"I was just reflecting on our trip to Galatia . . ."

---

1. Chapters 5 and 6, along with part of chapter 7, are a basic retelling of
Acts 13:13–14:28.

2. In this section, I have Manaen, Lucius, and Niger ask some rather
elementary questions. Given their role in the church in Antioch, it seems likely
that they would have been more advanced in their theological understanding,
and they would have known the history of this missionary journey since Paul
and Barnabas had debriefed the whole church upon their return. However,
rather than add characters, I decided to use them to bring out the meaning
of some of Paul's thoughts as well as the events of the journey.

The two men stood gazing out over the city. The many oil lamps made the otherwise dark shapes of the houses sparkle like the night sky. A soft breeze carried a mixed scent of fragrant blossoms and wood fires. Paul was slowly sipping from a cup of milk mixed with honey.

"There was a sense of urgency," Paul continued, "or, at least, I had a sense of urgency to leave Perga because the pass through the mountains would otherwise have been blocked with snow. As it is, it took us a week to reach the top. We had decided to take the longer route as it was newer and, for that reason, easier, but it was still very difficult for me.[3] I was so sick that I had to rely on Barnabas to help me find my way as my eyes had been affected by the illness. But our fellow Jews in Pisidian Antioch were so kind and welcoming and ever so ready to help me recover.[4] And they were hungry for the word – desperate for some message of encouragement."[5]

"What was it like . . . the actual city, I mean?" Manaen asked.

"Pisidian Antioch? Well, not like our Antioch at all! For one, it has a much higher elevation than our city, which has made it an important city for the Romans, despite it being rather isolated. They like places that give them a good vantage point to keep watch over the plains and over the main road crossing the highland from West to East. It gives them a sense of control. It is also home to relatives of both Caesar Tiberius and King Herod[6] – I suppose you knew that[7] – as well as many Roman

---

3. There were two trails up through the Taurus Mountains. One was shorter, the then recently constructed Via Sebaste, and the shorter trail leading directly north of Perga. Walker, *In the Steps*, 78.

4. Galatians 4:13–16.

5. Acts 13:14–15.

6. See Wall, *Acts*, 191, footnote 474.

7. Manaen would have been expected to know this since he had been brought up with Herod Antipas. Acts 13:1.

senators and aristocrats, including Sergius Paulus, the proconsul of Cyprus.[8] Nevertheless, it is a cold and miserable place."

"If it is so remote, why did you go there?"

"Well, mainly because Sergius Paulus came from there and had recommended us[9] but also because I was too sick to travel any further at that point; and don't forget, there is a sizeable Jewish community in the city."

"And the synagogue is a natural place for you to start, right?"

"Yes," Paul replied. "Always the Jews first, then the Gentiles.[10] It is a good beginning for us as we are talking to people who know the Scriptures well. Also, there are usually a number of God-fearers among them, and that helps to give us an open door into the Gentile community."

Niger and Lucius had joined them while Paul was speaking. They were both feasting on the fresh dates and the dried fig and raisin cakes Paul had bought earlier in the marketplace.

Niger swallowed what he was chewing and then asked, "For the sake of clarity, at least as far as the wording for the letter is concerned, remind us of what you taught them."

"Well, firstly you need to remember that *they* invited us to address them," Barnabas said, as he stepped up onto the flat roof. He offered Paul one of the raisin cakes he was carrying before continuing, "Perhaps it was the wretched weather or maybe it was because they lived among pagans who worshipped the emperor as a god, but they seemed to need a message of encouragement."

It was a cloudless night. The stars sparkled brightly in the ink-black sky, like millions of torches suspended in mid-air.

---

8. See Wright, *Paul: A Biography*, 117.

9. Wright, 120.

10. Acts 13:46.

The moon was just beginning to peek over the hills, creating a glowing silver line along the ridge.

"And I took full advantage of the invitation," Paul muttered with his mouth full of raisins, placing a hand in front of his face as he chuckled.

"That he did!" Barnabas said, laughing. "Didn't even think twice. He just got up and spoke to them as if it was the most normal thing in the world."

"Even though you were still not feeling well?" asked Niger, a note of admiration in his voice.

"Oh, by that time I was feeling a bit stronger. It was really just my eyes that were still bothering me."

"So, remind us. What *did* you say?" Manaen urged.

"Well, I started with our story as God's people . . . I wanted to start with something they already knew and then move forward to show them how Jesus was the climax of what God has always been doing in and through us."

"And you wanted to point out how merciful God has always been in spite of our repeated disobedience in the wilderness and in the land," Barnabas added. "And that it has always been God's mercy and infinite patience that has kept us as a nation."

"That's right," Paul said, washing down the sweet, sticky raisins with a drink of his warm milk. "Salvation has always started with God . . . it has always been his initiative. If anything, the story of our exodus from slavery in Egypt shows that we cannot deliver ourselves from anything!"

"And the period of the judges clearly demonstrates how we are just as predisposed to sin as all the other nations around us," Barnabas said sadly. "Nations, I might add, that our ancestors so desperately wanted to copy that they demanded a king in spite of the fact that God is our only true king!"

"But how did you introduce Jesus as the promised Saviour?" Lucius asked.

"Through King David," Paul replied, taking another bite of the raisin cake. "Every Jew knows that God had promised to raise up a ruler from the house of Jesse.[11] But I also emphasized the fact that David was made king after the disastrous reign of King Saul."

"Why is that so important?" Niger asked, puzzled.

"Because it once again reveals the need for God to raise up a *faithful* ruler after the failure of an *unfaithful* ruler. So, just as Israel had failed, so had their leaders."

Manaen, Niger, and Lucius stared at Paul blankly.

"In other words," Barnabas explained, "Jesus is like a greater David, raised up by God to do what David or any other leader could not do . . . indeed, what even the best of us could not do."

"Exactly," Paul said, stabbing the air with his forefinger as if to make a point. "You see, the thrust of my discourse was to show that our powerlessness to overcome sin necessitated the coming of Jesus. That's why I introduced him only after I had first demonstrated our inability to live as God had commanded us to live."

Paul drew in his breath sharply and then continued. "But before going any further, I reminded them of what John the Baptizer had said about the one coming after him. Most Jews, even in the diaspora, still revere John as a prophet and a martyr, and John's statement that he was not worthy to perform the task of the lowliest slave for Jesus indicates the prominence of the person of Jesus."

"So," Barnabas clarified, "using John's declaration, Paul prepared them for what he was about to tell them about Jesus."

---

11. Isaiah 11:1; Jeremiah 23:5–6; Amos 9:11.

"Yes, I can see that," Niger said, "but how did you explain the attitude of our leaders? They did not believe John or Jesus!"

"Well, I told them that our leaders did not recognize Jesus as Messiah," Paul replied. "But notice I did this only after I had connected Jesus with John's statement."

"That was clever," said Manaen, with a toothy grin. "That makes the leaders' rejection of Jesus a rejection of John . . . someone your listeners already respect."

"Yes, he is quite the master debater," Barnabas said, sucking the sticky residue off his fingers. "At this point, he brilliantly introduced the notion that the execution of Jesus was a fulfilment of the words of the prophets and then . . . would you believe it," Barnabas waved his hands dramatically, "then he left them hanging while he laid the groundwork for what he was about to reveal by telling them all about the witnesses to Jesus's resurrection."

"You must remember," Paul said, with a slightly embarrassed chuckle, "that, in one sense, I *was* one of those leaders who did not recognize Jesus! But now, there I stood before them, a testimony to something I had at first not understood myself. However, I also wanted to show that Scripture was as much a witness to Jesus as those who physically saw him raised from the dead, so I provided them with scriptural support for my position. I quoted from the Psalms[12] and the prophet Isaiah[13] to show that only one who was not subject to corruption could be Israel's Messiah. David had died, as did all his descendants, but Jesus had been raised from the dead to reign as an eternal king. As such, he alone can be the referent of the prophecy."

---

12. Psalms 2:7; 16:10.
13. Isaiah 55:3.

"That's brilliant!" Manaen said excitedly. "I need to remember your technique. You string them along with stories they already know, you get them to nod in agreement all along, and then, wham!" He struck his open palm with his fist. "You deliver the gospel firmly set in a familiar context."

"And that's precisely what he did," Barnabas stated. "But it is what Paul said next that is important for our current context."

"And that was?" Niger asked, leaning forward to listen more closely.

"I told them that only through the faithfulness of Jesus could anyone be declared just and that we could not be justified through observance of the law of Moses."

"Wow!" said Lucius, sucking in air. "That's a convoluted mouthful."

Paul continued as if he hadn't heard. "Remember, I had already showed them the impossibility of perfect obedience, from the exodus through the period of the judges and then the monarchy. So, the logical conclusion of the repeated failure of our ancestors is simply that pardon for sin – in other words, salvation or deliverance – can only be received by grace. It cannot be earned by merit because we, as members of the human race, are incapable of deserving it."

"Paul did leave them with something to think about though," Barnabas chimed in. "He quoted a warning taken from the prophet Habakkuk . . . that they ought not to be like those who had not believed what God had done in their days."[14]

"And how did they respond to that?" Lucius asked. "Is that when they stoned you?"

---

14. Habakkuk 1:5 – note that Paul appears to be quoting from the Septuagint (Ancient Greek) translation of the Hebrew Scriptures, which is why in most English translations Acts 13:41 is slightly different to Habakkuk 1:5.

"No," Paul said, shuddering as he remembered the incident. "No, that was later. At this point, most of them were quite gracious and asked us to return the following Sabbath. Many of the Jews and the God-fearers went with us and, throughout the week, kept asking us numerous questions." Paul sighed deeply and then, as if to himself, said softly, "I pleaded with them to continue in the grace of God. How could they now . . .?"

"So, what happened when you returned the next Sabbath?" Niger interrupted.

"Well," Paul said, roused from his thoughts, "that was when the trouble began. So many people from the city came to the synagogue to hear us, and when the Jews saw the great gathering, they became envious and began to argue vehemently against everything I was saying." Paul broke off and stared blankly into the night.

"And then . . .?" Manaen urged.

"We were rather bold," Barnabas filled in, "telling them that as they had rejected the free offer of eternal life, we would now turn our attention to the Gentiles."

"That must have made them angry," Lucius said, popping a large date into his mouth.

"Yes, but as justification for such a shocking statement, Paul quoted from the prophet Isaiah who clearly stated that Israel's purpose in being a light for the Gentiles was so that salvation would extend to the ends of the earth."[15]

"In this sense," Paul added, "the unbelieving Jews in Pisidian Antioch were doing exactly what the unbelieving leaders did in Jerusalem."

"How so?" Niger inquired.

---

15. Isaiah 49:6; see Acts 1:8.

"Well, through their rejection of the gospel, God's redemptive purposes were fulfilled," Paul stated simply. "Their rejection opened the door for us to focus our attention on the Gentiles. And all those whom God had chosen, just as he had chosen us, accepted the truth."

Paul swallowed the dried fig he was chewing, drank another mouthful of his milk mixture, and then continued. "But what was even more exciting was that our newborn disciples then began to copy us . . . doing what we were doing. They took our message and told their families and friends. Our disciples became disciple makers. And consequently, the word spread quickly throughout the area."

"That is exciting," Niger acknowledged, rubbing his chin. "I remember Peter telling us that Jesus taught his disciples this method of making disciples who could make disciples."

"But," Manaen interrupted, "what about the unbelieving Jews? I don't suppose they were happy about this."

"No, they were not," Barnabas said. "They got a number of important people to expel us from the city. Of course, that wasn't difficult. The Romans are always wary about any talk of a lord or a king other than Caesar."

"So, you just left?" Manaen asked.

"Not immediately, no," Paul replied. "We knew that our disciples there would face fierce opposition in the future, so we wanted to make sure that they knew the truth about Jesus and would be able to give a sound reason for their faith in him.[16] And we also wanted to demonstrate to them, first-hand, how to deal with conflict and persecution. As the wise teacher once said, 'There is a time to speak and a time to be silent.'[17] They

---

16. See 1 Peter 3:15.

17. Ecclesiastes 3:7b.

needed to know when to take advantage of a situation and when to retreat from it."

"So," Barnabas added, "now you can see, through what has happened, why we are so concerned. Young believers can be led astray quite easily by clever talk, especially if they are told that they are missing out on something not previously shared with them! Remember, that was the way the serpent tempted Eve. So, we endeavoured to teach them as much as we could, by both word and example."

"But," Paul interrupted, "it was more than simple knowledge and practical application of the Scriptures. We wanted to make sure that they understood what it means to be directed by the Holy Spirit daily.[18] To start every day with a submissive and a receptive heart, listening intently for his direction through reflection on God's word, sometimes even denying ourselves the pleasures of the body and fasting so that we might concentrate on the things of the Spirit."

"Yes," Barnabas added, "and so we taught them how to live prayerfully dependent lives like Jesus, who never did anything unless he heard from the Father.[19] We taught them how to focus their thoughts on living in obedience to the will of God[20] so that the name of God would always be exalted in everything they said and did."[21]

"And," Paul said, "we taught them how to be other-person-centred."

---

18. From conception to resurrection, Jesus was dependent on the ministry of the Holy Spirit. See Matthew 4:1; Mark 1:10; Luke 1:35; 3:22; 4:1, 14–15, 18; John 1:33–34; Romans 8:11; Hebrews 9:14.

19. John 5:19, 30; 8:28–29. See also Matthew 4:1–11; 14:13, 23; Luke 6:12–13; 22:39–46.

20. See John 13:12–17; Philippians 2:5–11.

21. See John 7:16–18; 17:1–4; Romans 12:1–2.

"What does other-person-centred mean?" Niger asked.

"It means that they ought to always think of others rather than only of themselves,"[22] Barnabas explained. "Even to regard others better than themselves. I really believe that was how Jesus managed to attract even the unholy.[23] By the way he treated everyone he met, they knew he cared about them personally."

"But eventually, the opposition was so intense that we had to leave," Paul said, helping himself to another small cake of figs. "So, we shook the dust off our feet in protest. That's a sign they all understood, as I think you do too. It's what we Jews do when leaving Gentile territory. And so, by our action, we demonstrated clearly that since they had refused God's blessing, the curse remained with them."

"But our disciples knew they were not alone," Barnabas said, smiling. "Our Lord was with them as he had promised.[24] They had been filled with the Holy Spirit, and we had taught them how to walk in step with him. And so, not even this unpleasantness could rob them of their newfound joy or stop them from passing on the good news to others."

---

22. Philippians 2:3. See also John 13:34–35; 15:13.
23. Matthew 11:19; Luke 7:34.
24. Matthew 28:18–20.

# 6

---

# Undeterred

Acts 14:1–20

Paul and Barnabas reflect on the difficulties
in preaching the gospel cross-culturally.
They explain the need for understanding
the host culture so as to avoid potential
misinterpretations and misunderstandings.

"And then you went to Iconium?" Lucius asked, sitting down on the low parapet around the roof.

"Yes," Paul replied.

"And . . .?"

"Well, something very similar happened there. Some believed, some didn't, and those who did not believe went out of their way to make trouble for us and for our disciples. But the Lord blessed us with his presence through many miraculous interventions."

"We stayed there for quite some time," Barnabas added, "until the opposition threatened to become violent. Then we fled to the Lycaonian cities of Lystra and Derbe."

Paul scratched his bald head. "If you recall, something happened there for which we were not prepared. Do you remember?"

"Wasn't that where the people did not understand you because they spoke a local dialect?" Niger offered.

"Not only that, but we had no reference point such as we'd always had in the local synagogues!" Barnabas said. "So, our familiar pattern of Jew first and then Gentile was broken. Paul reasoned as best he could by using their own stories in his preaching and teaching, but their customs were very foreign to us."

"And there's an important lesson for us in that," Paul said, once more stabbing the air with his forefinger. "Had we known about their religious views and their customs prior to our arrival, we might have done things a little differently."

"How so?" Lucius asked.

"We learned later," Barnabas explained, "that they believed a legend about the Greek gods Zeus and Hermes."

"Ah yes," Lucius said, "I remember now. They believed that in the past Zeus and Hermes had been denied hospitality except in the home of an elderly couple. The gods then destroyed the houses of those who had rejected them and blessed the old couple by making their home a temple."

"And was there a temple to these gods in Lystra?" Manaen asked, biting on a fingernail.

"Yes," Barnabas replied, "we saw it as we entered the city."

"We should have realized then that we ought to do things differently," Paul said wistfully.

"But Paul," Barnabas interrupted, "I must say, in our defence, that there were many pagan temples in every one of these cities, so this did not seem either strange or uncommon."

"Yes, that's true," Paul acquiesced, "but I seem to remember it was more active than most. Perhaps we ought to have been more prayerful . . . waited on the leading of the Holy Spirit instead of just barging on like I did."

"I'm not sure I would agree, Paul," Barnabas said. "I do believe it was the Holy Spirit who prompted you to heal that lame man."

"But *that* was what caused the misunderstanding, Barnabas," Paul said, waving his arms about. "It was because of this miraculous healing that the crowd mistook us for their gods."

"They started shouting in a language we did not understand," Barnabas told the others. "But when the priests arrived with their garlanded oxen, this young boy stepped out of the thronging masses and told us what they were saying. He told us that they were about to sacrifice the oxen in our honour. He told us that they were saying that I was Zeus and Paul was Hermes."

"Why did they associate you with Zeus and Paul with Hermes?" asked Niger.

"I'm not sure," Barnabas replied, "but I think it was because Paul did most of the speaking. You see, Hermes is considered Zeus's spokesperson."

"Of course, we were mortified," Paul said, shaking his head. "We did everything in our power to stop this blasphemous action. The young man served as my interpreter. I could tell he knew the Scriptures well, and I was grateful for his assistance."

"It was in the midst of all this confusion and shouting that some of the unbelieving Jews from Pisidian Antioch and Iconium arrived and incited the crowds against us," Barnabas said.

"And that was when they tried to stone you to death, Paul?" Lucius asked.

"Yes," Paul answered, rubbing his hand over his face and tugging lightly at his beard. "Right there and then. There was no warning. The first rock hit me hard on my cheek, and I tasted blood. I remember wondering what had just happened. It was so unexpected. When another stone hit me, I suddenly had this vivid image in my mind of Stephen's stoning. Remember, I had kept watch over those murderers' garments. I could have stopped them, but I did not. In fact, I was in full agreement with them then. And there I was . . . being stoned myself for the same reason Stephen was stoned to death."

Paul paused to take another sip of milk. He felt a cold sweat break out all over him. It was as if he was reliving that terrible moment. He swallowed, took a deep breath, and continued.

"Then followed a hail of stones, and people were shouting and throwing dust in the air. It was so strange . . . as if time itself had slowed down. I had this bizarre buzzing sound in my ears, and I could clearly hear my heart beating rapidly. Funny, I don't really remember feeling pain after the first couple of stones."

Paul paused once more, shaking his head as if in disbelief.

"I tried to get away, but the rocks were coming from all directions. One hit me hard right here on my temple." Paul indicated the spot with his hand. "I must have fainted because I do not remember them dragging me out of the city."

"We thought he was dead," Barnabas said solemnly. "But after the crowd had calmed down, they walked back into the city, leaving Paul's body in a ditch on the side of the road. We crept out of our hiding places to retrieve what we thought was a corpse."

"Who was with you?" Niger asked. "I thought it was just you and Paul."

"No," Barnabas replied. "Sorry, I know that's how it sounds when we tell the story, but there were disciples of ours who had come along with us from Pisidian Antioch and Iconium. This was all part of their training as disciples, you see. That's what Jesus did with his disciples. He would take them with him on his journeys and show them how to do the work of the ministry."

"So, what did you all do when you found that Paul was not dead?" Manaen asked, still biting on his fingernail.

Barnabas clasped his hands together and peaked his two index fingers before his face, blowing his breath out between his palms. "Well, naturally, we were overjoyed. But he was in such a state . . . blood everywhere. Nothing like the bleeding of head wounds. His clothes were torn, and he was bruised all over, and covered in dust. We didn't quite know what to do, to be honest, but then that young man who had served as Paul's interpreter stepped forward and took us to his mother's home. Her name was Eunice, and they lived there together with his grandmother, Lois. These were two remarkable Jewish women, and they had taught this young man well."

"What was his name?" Niger inquired. "And did they believe the gospel?"

"Yes, they believed," Paul said, reaching again for his milk. "And they really knew the Scriptures well and understood every connection we made between what was written and the truth about Jesus."

"And his name?" Niger asked again.

Paul smiled. "His name is Timothy."

# 7

# Of Fools and Promises

Acts 14:21–28; Galatians 3:1–19

> With arguments from the life of Abraham,
> Paul demonstrates that salvation has always
> been based on the faithfulness of God. As
> the promise was fulfilled in the life and
> ministry of Jesus, so all who believe in him
> are, collectively, the one seed of Abraham.

So, after Derbe, did you go back the way you came?" Manaen asked, as they climbed down the steps from the roof to the floor below.

"Yes," Barnabas said, balancing the wooden trays that held the leftover food. "We wanted to make sure the disciples in each city understood that the way ahead would not be an easy one. We appointed leaders in every community, and then we prayed and fasted with them, committing them to the Lord in whom they had trusted. And then, before sailing back here, we preached in Perga because we had not done so earlier in our haste to get through the mountain pass before the snows."

"And yet," said Paul sadly, "after all that teaching, not to mention the demonstration of the Holy Spirit's power, these Galatians have fallen foul to false teachers."

"They must be fools to be so blind!" Niger said, trying to settle into a comfortable scribal position once more.

"Or they have been bewitched by the evil eye," Lucius offered. "I have heard of such things in the pagan lands."

"From what you've just told us," Manaen said, "it seems that you did everything in your power to vividly portray and expound on the meaning of the passion story in your teaching."

"One thing," Paul said, his index finger pointed upward, "one thing I would ask of them if I could. Did they receive the Holy Spirit through observing the law or by trusting in the faithfulness of God?"

"If they answer that question truthfully," Barnabas said, "you would have to say no more."

"Oh, Barnabas," Paul said, his voice cracked with emotion, "can they really be so foolish? They received the Holy Spirit apart from the requirements of the law, so why would they now wish to try and earn through human effort what has been freely given?"

"Just think of how much they suffered already because of their newfound faith!" Barnabas shook his head in disbelief. "Was that all for nothing?"

"Hopefully not for nothing," Paul said flatly. "But I say again, they will have to answer this question: Did God pour out his Spirit on them – indeed, does he, even now, perform all manners of wonders among them – because they scrupulously fulfilled the requirements of the law or because they trusted in his faithfulness?"

Niger spoke. "If they recall their initial response to your message, surely the absurdity of their skewed thinking will be self-evident?"

"Abraham!" Paul blurted out, suddenly becoming animated, his eyes shining with the unexpected insight. "Abraham believed God, and that is why God declared him righteous. In the same way, it is those who believe who are reckoned Abraham's offspring. The Scriptures . . . Barnabas!"

In his excitement, Paul grabbed his colleague by the shoulders and beamed into his eyes. "The Scriptures predicted that one day God would declare the nations just by his faithful fulfilment of the promise made to Abraham. And so, the gospel was preached to and through Abraham! 'All nations will be blessed in you,' God said.[1] So, it is those who rely on God's faithfulness who are blessed along with the faithful Abraham!"

"Yes!" Barnabas said, picking up on Paul's elation. "In fact, one can also say that those who rely on their own efforts to keep the law are under a curse because it is written that those who do not continue in everything written in the book of the law are cursed!"[2]

"Exactly!" Paul crowed. "Not such a strong word now, is it? But my point is that it is clear that no one can be declared just by the works of the law because the Scriptures plainly state that the just live because of *his* faithfulness![3] But law observance is not the same as God's faithfulness. Just the opposite! The law can

---

1. Genesis 12:3.

2. Deuteronomy 27:26.

3. Habakkuk 2:4. As Paul appears to have used the Septuagint (Ancient Greek) version of the Old Testament – judging by the minor difference in his quotations, I have chosen to use this version here. In other words, the just shall live by my (God's/his) faithfulness.

only give life to those who keep it all, and that is impossible![4] Christ redeemed us . . . Niger, are you getting this?"

"I'm trying," came the plaintive reply, as Niger scribbled away on the parchment.

"Christ redeemed us," continued Paul, who, having let go of Barnabas, was now pacing up and down across the room. "Christ redeemed us from this curse of the law by taking that curse upon himself! It is written: Cursed is everyone who is hung from a tree.[5] So the blessing of Abraham has come to the Gentiles through Christ Jesus since the promise of the Spirit is received because of his faithful obedience."

"Wait! Wait!" Manaen cried out. "I'm not following you. How does what you have just said make the Gentiles the offspring of Abraham?"

Paul paused to reflect. He closed his eyes as if the darkness would help him to think more clearly.

"Alright, brethren, let's put it like this. Here's an example from day-to-day life. Once a will has been confirmed, no one can add to it, right?"

"Ye-es," Manaen replied, "but what's that got to do with . . ."

"Let me finish. Once a will has been confirmed, no one can add to it, right?"

"Right," they all said together.

"So," Paul declared, clapping his hands together with glee, "the promises were given to Abraham and his seed . . . the word 'seed' is singular, not plural. Seed, not seeds. One, not many. And that one seed is Christ, as well as all who are in him, Jew and Gentile alike! There can only be one body, just as there is only one Spirit . . . one Lord, one faith, one entrance into the

---

4. Leviticus 18:5.
5. Deuteronomy 21:23; 27:26.

covenant . . . because we have only one God who is Father of all . . . over all, through all, in all."[6]

"But don't the teachers say that the one seed was Isaac?" Manaen sounded perplexed.

"Yes," Barnabas answered, "but we believe that Jesus is the climax and fulfilment of the promise made to Abraham. We believe that he is the one seed . . . and, therefore, those who are in the one seed must also be one. God's promise to Abraham was for one family, not many."[7]

"So," Paul continued as if he hadn't heard the interruption, "my point is this: the confirmed will of Abraham cannot be rendered null and void by a law that came 430 years later! The law cannot void the promise. Don't you see?"

Paul looked at them with a wide, toothy smile, his eyes glowing with delight. "If the inheritance came by the law, it would invalidate the promise, right? But God has given it to Abraham by the promise!"

"Therefore, the law cannot repeal the promise!" Manaen said excitedly. "That's brilliant!"

"Uhm, Paul?"

"Yes, Lucius?"

"I have a question."

"Yes?"

"Why then the law?"

---

6. Ephesians 4:5–6.

7. I think there is a double application of the idea of "one seed." The one seed is not only the Messiah but also all those who are "in" him. Paul later refers to the lack of divisions in the church. See Wright, *Paul and the Faithfulness of God*, 868.

# 8

---

# From Prisoners to Heirs

Galatians 3:19–4:7

> Paul compares the law to a legal guardian of
> an underage beneficiary – a guardian who is
> no longer needed because the Son and heir has
> now come, bringing the time of immaturity to
> an end. Through adoption, God has made us
> his children, united as one family in Jesus.

"Why then the law, you ask?" Paul echoed the question as he searched his brain for a clear answer. "Why then the law? Well, I believe the law was given to counteract lawlessness until the fulfilment of the promise."

"I think I understand," Lucius said. "While in Egypt, Israel had succumbed to the false religion of their masters and embraced a corresponding lifestyle. So God gave them the law to direct them away from falsehood into truth . . . as an aid to help them embrace a new way of life and unlearn the old. It was given as a corrective so that his delivered people might live in freedom instead of in bondage."

Lucius looked at Paul inquiringly.

Paul smiled, his eyes twinkling. "But what did Israel do with the law?"

"I think that Israel made what was meant to be a corrective into a directive and, by doing so, they allowed the law to supplant the promise. They put the cart before the horse . . . and the Galatians are now making the same mistake. Am I right?"

Paul drew in his breath, paused, and then continued. "Yes, the law was given to a people *already delivered* by God and yet, still in need of redirection by God away from the lifestyle of human servitude. Deliverance, or to continue with what I have been saying, the promise preceded the giving of the law. As you said, they put the cart before the horse. But we must also bear in mind that while God gave the law to us through the mediation of Moses, the promise was given directly to Abraham by God himself. Mediation is beneficial when there is more than one party involved, but the promise was unmediated because God is one."

"Are you saying that the law is in opposition to the promise?" Niger asked.

Paul raised his eyebrows. "Definitely not! But we need to put things in their proper place. If there was a law that could generate new life, then things would have been put right through law observance. However, Scripture tells us that we are like those who have been imprisoned – imprisoned by the power of sin – and that the promised deliverance can only come to those who trust in the faithfulness of Jesus Christ."

"Niger," Barnabas interjected, "think of it this way. It is like the exodus from Egypt. As slaves, we could not escape because we had been imprisoned by a power greater than ourselves, but we were delivered in due time because God was faithful to the promise he made to Abraham. We did not free ourselves because we could not free ourselves. God alone liberated us from prison and enslavement."

"That's right," Paul continued, "and in the same way, before the promised deliverance through Jesus Christ was fulfilled, we were all kept locked up by the law, in protective custody if you will, until his faithful fulfilment was made known to us. In this sense, the law is just like the slave who is appointed to be our guardian while we are underage.[1] But now, because of Jesus's faithfulness, faithfulness even to death on the cross,[2] we are no longer in need of a guardian since in Christ Jesus you are all made children of God."

Paul paused. "Niger, would you read that back to me, please?"

Niger read what he had written. "In the same way, before . . . we are no longer in need of a guardian since, in Christ Jesus, you are all made children of God."

"All!" Paul exclaimed, clapping his hands together, making everyone jump. He began to speak very fast, pacing back and forth across the room again. "As many of you as were baptized into Christ have been covered by Christ and are united in Christ. There are no more divisions. You are all made one in Christ Jesus. There are no more distinctions. No more prejudices! One seed, one body. No longer are we divided into ethnic categories, like Jews and Greeks. No more class divisions, like slaves and freemen. There is no longer any form of discrimination even between genders!" Paul looked around at them, his face aglow with exhilaration. "Don't you see? If you are in Christ, then,

---

1. See the note on Galatians 3:24 in the *NRSV Cultural Backgrounds Study Bible*, 2066–2067.

2. Philippians 2:8.

through him, you also are the seed of Abraham and heirs of that promise."

"Slow down, Paul, please," Niger complained.

"I can't," Paul said, laughing. "Think on this!" Paul was once more stabbing the air with his index finger. "As long as we are underage, we are no better than our slave-guardian, even though we actually own him as well as the rest of the property, right? As long as we are underage, we remain under this slave's tutelage and custody until the fullness of the time set by our parent arrives."

Everyone had stopped moving, as if immobilized by what Paul was saying.

"Well, don't you see?" Paul continued, his voice rising an octave higher. "The same is true for us as far as our salvation is concerned. We were like children, governed by the elementary spiritual principles of the old world. But now, brothers!"

Paul spun around like a whirling top, clapped his hands together again, and shouted, "Now the time has fully come! As promised, God sent his Son, the seed of a woman,[3] subject to the law, to release us from the custody of the law so that we might receive adoption as children!"

"Yes!" Barnabas cried out, equally excited as he grasped the gravity and beauty of what Paul was saying. "Yes, just like God adopted Israel[4] and promised us an inheritance,[5] so he has adopted us and made us his heirs!"

"But because we are his children," Paul was laughing and weeping simultaneously. "Because we are his children, God has filled our hearts with the Spirit of his Son[6] and, in us, this Spirit

3. Genesis 3:15.

4. Exodus 4:22; Romans 9:4.

5. Deuteronomy 26:1.

6. See Ezekiel 36:26–28.

cries out, 'Abba, Father!' We are no longer subject to our slave-guardian." Paul stifled a sob of pure joy. "We are God's children. And as his children, we are heirs of God through Christ!"

For a moment, stunned silence descended on the group like a thick blanket, but then, as one man, they threw it off as they spontaneously burst into declarations of praise.

# 9

## A Cry for Freedom

Galatians 4:8–5:1

Using the Old Testament story of Ishmael and Isaac – Abraham's two sons – as a metaphor, Paul argues that we are not children born of human effort but children born of God's promise. He likens the Galatians' desire to return to the images and shadows of the promise that was realized in Jesus to Abraham and Sarah's effort to produce a son through means apart from the divine promise.

I am beginning to appreciate Moses's frustration with the Israelites in the wilderness," Paul said, as he sat on the floor, leaning against the wall.

"Because of their desire to return to Egypt?" Lucius asked.

"Yes." Paul sighed. "These Galatians – at least the Gentile Galatians – were once enslaved by gods that required constant placation through multiple rituals and requirements. But now that they have come to a relational knowledge of the one true

God – or rather, now that the one true God in his grace knows them – they desire to return to the shadows and images of the past that have been fulfilled in the present! How can they want to return to slavery?"

Paul felt a hot tear roll down his face. He loved them. He really loved them, and his heart ached for them. They were like the children he had never had. Was this how Moses had felt, too? When the Israelites had turned away from the God who had delivered them so spectacularly to serve the golden calf and heavenly bodies and the idols of the nations around them, it must have hurt him deeply. He recalled Moses's intercessory prayer. Moses had even been willing to have his name erased from the Book of Life for the sake of Israel.[1]

"You know, Paul," Barnabas said, "this tendency to exchange the relational face-to-face worship God desires for elementary rituals – new moons, sabbaths, various festivals – has been a regular and recurring problem in the life of our people. Think of what God said through the prophet Isaiah. 'I cannot endure the new moons, sabbaths, convocations and the calling of assemblies! I abhor your new moons and seasonal feasts. These things are burdensome to me, and I am weary of them.'[2] This seems to be a problem that is common to the human heart."

"Ah, Barnabas," Paul groaned, "I am afraid I have laboured in vain and exhausted my strength for nothing."

The group sat in silence for a long while, their earlier expressions of exuberant joy now swallowed up in a sea of sorrow.

"I want to appeal to our brethren," Paul said suddenly. "I want to beg them to imitate me . . . to be as I am. They have

---

1. Exodus 32:32.
2. Isaiah 1:13–14.

not wronged me. To the contrary, as I said earlier, they cared for me in spite of the fact that my illness placed a burden on them. They did not reject me then, so why are they rejecting me now? They welcomed me as if I were an angel of God – or, indeed, Christ himself! What has happened to that goodness? You know, they would have gone to any length to bless me, even sacrificing their own eyes![3] Why have I now become their enemy because I speak the truth?"

"I'm not sure they think of you as an enemy, Paul," Manaen offered. "I think what has happened is that those false teachers flatter them because they wish to alienate them from you so that the Galatians will shift their allegiance to them. It's a form of manipulation."

"Well," Paul said, rubbing his bald head once more, "flattery is not always bad, but it is even better when the flattery is presented in your absence in your defence."

Another tear rolled down his cheek. "I feel like a mother giving birth all over again. You know, I really do see them as my very own children. I feel once again the same pain I felt for them then, desperately desiring that they be fully developed in the womb of Christ. How I wish I was present with them and could change my speech to a more conciliatory tone. I am stunned by what they are doing!"

They sat in silence for a brief period again, then Paul suddenly jumped up, pointed a finger at an imaginary speaker and said, "So, you who want to place yourselves under the law, let me tell you what the law says!"

"Write, Niger," Barnabas said, chuckling. "Write as fast as you can. There's no stopping him now!"

---

3. This remark by Paul could mean that the Galatians were willing to physically give him their eyes because of his weak eyesight or this might have been an idiom to express intense affection.

"It is written," Paul continued, "that God promised that Abraham would have a son . . . well, Abraham had two sons. One from a slave girl and the other from his wife. The first was conceived through the union of Abraham and his wife's handmaiden because Abraham and Sarah thought that what God had promised was not possible. But God *was* faithful to his promise, and so the second son was born to Sarah, his wife."

Paul began to pace again, still staring his imaginary challenger in the eye.

"Now, allow me to use this as a metaphor. These women are like two covenants. Hagar represents Mount Sinai, bringing forth children for enslavement. Hagar, like Mount Sinai in Arabia, corresponds with present day Jerusalem because her children are slaves like herself. But the other woman corresponds with the heavenly Jerusalem – she is our mother, and because she is free, so are we!"

Paul threw his arms up in the air as he quoted from the prophet Isaiah. "It is written: 'Sing for joy, you who are barren; break out into song and shout aloud, you who have never been in labour! Because the offspring of the unfruitful woman will be more in number than those who are married!'[4]"

He dropped his arms and began to interrogate his invisible challenger once more.

"We, beloved brethren, are like Isaac. We are children of the promise. And these false teachers are like the child born of human effort, who persecuted the child born of the Spirit. But tell me, what does the Scripture say? 'Let the slave and her son be expelled, for the son of the enslaved will not inherit with the son of the free.'[5] Likewise, dearest brethren, we are not children

---

4. Isaiah 54:1.

5. Genesis 21:10.

of the slave but children of the free! Christ has set us free for freedom. Stand your ground then, and do not be ensnared once again into slavery."

# 10

# Obligation or Love?

Galatians 5:2–6:18; Acts 15:2

In his closing remarks, Paul points out that
true fulfilment of the law is love in action.

Paul was still pacing as he dealt with his unseen challenger.
Niger was scribbling down as much as he could, as fast as
he could. It seemed to the group as if Paul had entered his own
world of thought and debate. No one else spoke a word.

"Seriously, I, Paul, say to you all, if you submit to
circumcision, there is no benefit for you in Christ. I bear witness
to the truth that if you submit to one part of the law – if you let
yourselves be circumcised – then you are required to submit
to every part of the law . . . that is if you wish to use the law as
a means to be justified. Should this be the case, then you will
turn your back on his grace as you will have cut yourselves off
from Christ.[1] Because of his faithfulness, we eagerly anticipate

---

1. By resorting to the law for salvation, the Galatians were effectively
denying the faithful fulfilment of God's promise in and through Christ.

in the Spirit the hope of being declared right before God. Don't you get it? Neither circumcision nor uncircumcision can be of benefit to you because you are in Christ Jesus, and his love has been demonstrated through his faithfulness."[2]

Paul sighed deeply. With a note of sadness in his voice, he said, "You were running your race so well. Who dissuaded you from pressing on in the truth? This kind of coaching is not in keeping with the one who is calling you. The whole lump of dough is leavened with just a tiny piece of leaven."

Paul shook his head. "But I am confident that those of you who are in the Lord will not be persuaded otherwise. Those placing hurdles in your way will bear their own penalty, whoever they may be."[3]

He suddenly stood still, eyes closed, deep in thought. Niger glanced over at Barnabas, but Barnabas just smiled and raised his eyebrows as if to say, wait for it.

"Think on this, my dearest brethren," Paul continued, more measured in his tone. "If, as they claim,[4] I neglected to teach you something I still teach others – that you must be circumcised – then why am I still being persecuted? For in that case, then the stumbling block of the cross would have been removed. Those causing doubt among you will themselves be cut off!"[5]

---

2. I believe that this is the meaning of the sentence since it is precisely what God said to Israel in Deuteronomy 7:7–9 – that he had delivered them for no other reason than his love for them and his faithfulness to his promise to Abraham.

3. Matthew 5:29–30; 18:6; Mark 9:42–48.

4. I have added the words "as they claim" here because it seems that Paul had to defend himself against a charge of neglect – that is, that while commanding others to be circumcised, he had neglected to teach this command to the Galatians.

5. When *ophelon* (wish/desire) is coupled with a future tense, it does not express a wish but, rather, states what is the logical outcome of the present. See Rendall, *Epistle to the Galatians*, 185.

"Yes," Barnabas agreed, interrupting Paul for the first time. "Well put. That is the law. Those who are false witnesses will receive the punishment intended for the accused."[6]

Emboldened by Barnabas, Manaen asked, "But is there not a danger that the Galatians will abandon the law altogether? Surely that is not what you want, is it?"

"No," Paul replied thoughtfully. "But, brethren, we are called in freedom to live in freedom."

"Yes," Manaen conceded, "but you are not saying that we can now abuse this freedom as an opportunity to fulfil the desires of the flesh, are you?"

"No," Paul agreed, "but I *am* saying that they ought to use the freedom they have as an opportunity to lovingly serve each other. That is the law. You well know that the entire law can be summed up in a single commandment, namely, love your neighbour as yourself. But if they compete aggressively with each other in their zeal for the law, they run the risk of consuming one another."

"So," Lucius said, "what you are saying is that there is a difference between doing what is right out of obligation or fear and doing what is right out of a sense of love and compassion."

"That's right," Barnabas interjected. "We do not abandon the law, but we obey it for very different reasons than those given by the false teachers. We obey it because we *are* free, not because we want to *be* free."

"Precisely!" Paul was practically shouting as he clapped his hands together above his head. "What I'm saying is that if you order your behaviour by the Spirit, you will not indulge in the

---

6. I believe Paul is referring to Deuteronomy 19:15–21, which orders that a false witness receive the punishment meant for the accused (see also Exod 20:16). In this case, those seeking to have the Galatians circumcised would, themselves, be "cut off."

desires of the flesh. The flesh strives against the Spirit because these are two conflicting forces. The different manifestations of the flesh and the Spirit are so glaringly obvious that it helps us decide against doing as we may please. And so, being led by the Spirit, we do not need to be restrained by the law."

"The prophets Jeremiah and Ezekiel told us that a time would come when the law would be written on our hearts,"[7] Barnabas explained. "Before we received new and clean hearts . . . before we received God's life-giving Spirit . . . before we were regenerated . . . we could *not* restrain ourselves. *That* was why the law was given then. It was given because of our hard hearts.[8] The law was not given to save us but to keep us from total abandonment to sin."

"That's right," Paul said. "The unregenerate person instinctively inclines to things like adultery, infidelity, impurity, lecherousness, idolatry, sorcery, animosity, clashes, self-centred intrigues, resentment, rivalries, divisions, sectarianism, envy, murder, drunkenness, debauchery, and the like. And I already warned them that those who habitually practise this way of life cannot be heirs of the kingdom of God. But, in stark contrast, the fruit produced by living and walking in step with the Spirit is love, joy, peace, patience, kindness, goodness, faithfulness, humility, and self-control. There is no law against this way of life."

Niger stopped writing and indicated that he wanted to ask a question.

"Yes, Niger?"

---

7. Jeremiah 31:31–34; Ezekiel 11:19–20; 36:25–27.

8. See also Matthew 19:8.

"I understand what you are saying in theory, Paul. But how does this work? How is it that we who are now regenerate in the Spirit do what is right out of love?"

"That's a good question," Paul replied. "Let me think. How can I put it?"

Paul stood still for a while, drumming his fingers on his lips as he formulated his reply. "Let me put it this way. For those of us who now belong to Christ, our old unregenerate inclinations have been crucified with him, along with all its passions and lusts. Consequently, if we have life *by* the Spirit we ought to live *in* the Spirit."

"Perhaps," began Lucius, rubbing his chin as he spoke, "the false teachers want to use the law as a means for self-elevation? You know, you have often said that what drove you to keep the law so meticulously was so that you would be better than your contemporaries."

"Indeed," Paul agreed, "as I said earlier, that is why I feel so strongly about what has been done by these false teachers. All of us must refrain from seeking self-elevation through contention and jealous envy."

"But, Paul," Barnabas said, holding a finger in the air as if to stop Paul, "they will need to know how to deal with those who have already submitted to this error."

"Yes," Paul nodded. "So, write this Niger. Brethren, if someone has yielded to error, you who are Spirit-led ought to restore them in all humility, considering yourselves as equally prone to yielding to such temptation. Support and encourage each other and thereby fulfil the law of Christ. If you think you are better than others then you are misguided, because we are all nothing. Let there be no occasion for unhealthy competitiveness for each one ought to be in control of their own behaviour."

"You know," Barnabas added, "as you were speaking about self-elevation and contention and envy and unhealthy competitiveness, I was reminded of the reason for tithing.[9] Israel tithed in order that the Levites and priests could freely perform their sacramental and teaching duties.[10] When the people failed to give a tenth of their produce to the temple, the priests were forced to provide for themselves . . . and hence their study of the law and teaching of the law was neglected, and so the people fell into lawless behaviour.[11] This principle is still applicable today: Those who benefit from the teaching of their leaders ought to support them well so that they will be free to teach them the truth. Perhaps those who lead the churches in Galatia are so preoccupied with their survival that they do not have time to study and apply the Scriptures."

"That may well be the case," Paul agreed. Then, reflecting on what Barnabas had said about the reasons for tithing, he added, "Those who are taught the word ought to share all things in common with their teachers so that these teachers will be able to give wise instruction that will help believers not to be misled. God will not be mocked. We will reap what we sow. The one who cultivates in the fields of self-centredness will reap corruption, whereas the one who cultivates in the field of the Spirit will, through the Spirit, reap eternal life."

"That sounds like the teaching of Jesus about where we should store treasures," Manaen said. "If your treasures are earthly, they are subject to theft and decay."

---

9. In Galatians 6, there seems to be an abrupt change in thought from verse 5 to verse 6. I have added a statement by Barnabas to knit together the teaching on behaviour with the teaching on supporting teachers in the church.

10. Numbers 18:21–32.

11. See Paul's argument in 1 Corinthians 9, especially verses 13–14.

"Yes," Lucius agreed. "And where we store our treasures serves as a good indication of what our priorities are in life . . . what is truly most important to us."

"That's right, Lucius," Paul said. "We should never weaken in our resolve to do good for, in due course, we will reap a reward if we do not give up. So then, while we still have time, let us work together for the benefit of all, especially for those who are members of the household of those who hold to the faith."

"Paul," Niger said, standing up once more, "my calves are cramping again. Could we stop for a moment?"

"You've done well, Niger," Paul said, beaming at the younger man. "I think I have said what I wanted to say. Let me look over what you have written, and I will add something personal. We do need to send this out as soon as possible."

Niger stretched and hobbled tenderly across the room to look out over the sleeping city, now enveloped in darkness. Clouds had crept across the sky, blocking out the light of the stars and the moon. He glanced back to see Paul holding the scroll close to his face. Then Paul took up the quill and began to write, speaking slowly as he wrote.

"Now, see in what large letters I write with my own hand. Those who seek to avoid being persecuted by those who find the cross repulsive, they now urge you to submit to the rituals of Judaism so that they might hold you up as trophies. By accepting Christ, these law-centred Jewish converts acknowledged that they were unable to keep the whole law; yet, they now seek to persuade you Gentile converts to be circumcised so that they might boast in your surrender to things that are merely ethnic distinctions."

Paul paused for a moment, then added, "But may I never be found to boast in anything except the cross of our Lord Jesus Christ, through which the old things of the world have no power over me and no longer attract me. Consequently, neither circumcision nor uncircumcision have any value in Christ because what matters is that, in him, we are new creations."

Again, Paul paused, staring up at nothing in particular. Then he looked down once more, speaking as he wrote, "Those who regulate their lives according to this rule have received peace and mercy and are therefore confirmed as the true Israel of God. As for the rest, let no one challenge me anymore because . . ."

Paul stopped and whispered, as if to himself, "like the slaves who willingly received the mark of perpetual servitude . . ."[12]

He then continued to write, "because my body has been branded with the mark of Christ."[13]

"That is deeply moving, Paul," Barnabas said, his eyes moist. "Our wounds are his wounds. If they persecuted our Lord, they will persecute us as well. We identify with his suffering and are identified by our participation in it."[14]

Paul sighed and looked up at his companion. "I once persecuted him."

Tears welled up in his eyes and rolled down his cheeks. A distressed donkey brayed loudly somewhere in the streets below.

"You know," Paul continued, after regaining his composure, "Ananias told me that when Jesus spoke to him in the vision, he

---

12. Exodus 21:6.

13. I do not think Paul was referring to a physical brand or mark on his body. Rather, in keeping with the rest of the Epistle, he contrasts the physical mark of circumcision – that enslaves one to the whole law – with the spiritual mark of perpetual servanthood to the one who has set us free by means of a new creation.

14. John 15:18–21.

had said that he would reveal to me how much I would suffer for the sake of his name.[15] This is only the beginning."

"I remember," Barnabas said. "He also said you are his chosen instrument to carry his name to the Gentiles and to their rulers, as well as to our people."

"There will be many more adventures," Paul said, smiling wistfully, "and many more scars."

He looked down at the scroll again and added, "The grace of our Lord Jesus Christ be with your spirit, brethren. Amen."

"Amen," they said in unison.

"Brothers," Paul said, standing up and stretching, "it is done. We have written our letter to our brethren in Galatia, and we only have a few hours left for sleep."

Paul began to walk towards the door. He stopped, turned, and then added, "Tomorrow, we leave for Jerusalem."

"Tomorrow?" Barnabas queried.

"Yes," Paul replied. "We have a meeting to attend, and it will take us at least a week to get there."

---

15. Acts 9:16.

# Short Biographies

## In order of appearance

**Paul** – Also known by his Hebrew name Saul (Acts 13:9), Paul was born (about AD 5) a Roman citizen in Tarsus[1] to a family of tent-making (Acts 18:3–4) Pharisees (Acts 23:6) of the tribe of Benjamin (Philippians 3:5). We know nothing more about his family other than that he had a married sister and a nephew in Jerusalem at the time of his arrest in that city (Acts 23:16). He was educated "according to the strict manner of the law" in Jerusalem under Gamaliel (Acts 22:3), grandson of the great Hillel, and, following the martyrdom of Stephen, he became the leading persecutor of the Early Church. On his way to Damascus to arrest believers in that city, Paul met the risen Jesus (about AD 35) and was subsequently commissioned to be a witness for the Gospel. He spent about three years in Arabia, after which he returned to Damascus where he was forced to leave under cover of darkness due to the negative response to his preaching of the unbelievers in the city (2 Corinthians 11:33). At first not well received in Jerusalem because people did not trust him as a former persecutor, Paul met with Peter and James, Jesus's brother (Galatians 1:19) after Barnabas vouched for him. Because of further violent threats, the church in Jerusalem thought it best for him to return to Tarsus, where he apparently spent several years witnessing in Cilicia and Syria (Acts 9:30; 15:41; Galatians 1:21). As the church in Antioch was

---

1. Tarsus was well known for raising goats that produced a high-quality goats' hair cloth used for tentmaking.

fast becoming an ethnically mixed community of believing Jews and Gentiles, Barnabas brought Paul to serve in Antioch. It was in Antioch that the Holy Spirit spoke clearly to the leadership of the church, setting Barnabas and Paul aside for missionary work elsewhere. Three major mission trips are documented in Scripture, but it is possible that after the imprisonment recorded in the closing chapter of the book of Acts (about AD 60–62) that Paul was released and that he went to Spain as he had planned (Romans 15:23–28).[2] According to Tertullian, Paul was beheaded under the persecution of Nero that took place after the great fire in Rome in AD 64.[3]

**Barnabas** – Barnabas was a Levite (Acts 4:36) whose family had moved to Cyprus. It is possible that he may have been a teacher of the law in a synagogue on the island. John Mark was his cousin (Colossians 4:10). His Jewish name was Joseph, but the apostles named him Barnabas (Acts 4:36) which means "son of encouragement." Contrary to the law (Joshua 13:33; 14:4), Barnabas owned a piece of land which he sold to alleviate the burden of those who were in need. According to Acts 9:27, it was Barnabas who recommended Paul to the apostles after his return to Jerusalem from Damascus. When the church in Antioch began to grow cross-culturally, the church in Jerusalem sent Barnabas to encourage the believers there, probably because Peter was already travelling. We are

---

2. I Clement 5:5–7; The Muratorian Canon 34–39; Cyril of Jerusalem, Catechesis, Lecture 17.26; Chrysostom, Second Timothy, Homily 10; Jerome, Amos, cap.5.

3. Tertullian, Scorpiace 15:4; The Prescription Against Heretics 36; See also Clement (1 Clement 5:5–7); Ignatius (Letter to the Ephesians 12:2); Polycarp (Letter to the Philippians 9:1–2); Dionysius of Corinth (Eusebius, Ecclesiastical History 2.25.4); Irenaeus (Against Heresies 3.1.1); The Acts of Paul.

told that he was a righteous man, full of the Holy Spirit, and of faith (Acts 11:24). After being in Antioch for a while, Barnabas decided to fetch Paul from Tarsus (Acts 11:25–26) to serve with him in Antioch. When the prophet Agabus predicted a great famine, the church in Antioch chose to send aid to the church in Jerusalem through Barnabas and Paul (Acts 11:27–30). Later, the Holy Spirit set apart Barnabas and Paul to take the Gospel to the Gentiles (Acts 13:1–3) and they took John Mark with them (Acts 15:5b) who later left them in Perga (Acts 13:13). While ministering in Lystra, Barnabas was mistakenly identified by the local population as Zeus (Acts 14:12.) Interestingly, Luke referred to him as an apostle in Acts 14:14. On their return to Antioch, Barnabas was temporally influenced by Peter in the presence of Jewish believers from Jerusalem to avoid eating with the Gentile believers (Galatians 2:11–14). Together with several other believers from Antioch, he then accompanied Paul to attend the council in Jerusalem where the matter of Gentile inclusion in the church was to be decided (Acts 15). Following the council and their return to Antioch, Paul wanted to revisit the churches established in Galatia. Barnabas wanted to take along his cousin, John Mark. Paul vehemently opposed this choice and so the team decided to go separate ways. John Mark went with Barnabas to Cyprus.

Barnabas is only mentioned once more in the Scriptures (1 Corinthians 9:5–6). Because of this positive reference to the ministry of Barnabas, some scholars assume that the two former co-workers had been reconciled at some point. John Mark served Paul while the apostle was a prisoner in Rome which may indicate that Barnabas was no longer alive at that time (Colossians 4:10). According to Christian tradition, Barnabas was martyred at Salamis. The Cypriot Orthodox Church claims him as their founder.

**Gamaliel** – Gamaliel I (died AD 52) was a leading teacher of the Jewish Oral Law. He was the son of Simeon and the grandson of the well-known sage Hillel. According to tannaitic tradition[4] he was their successor as president of the Sanhedrin. He was the first to be given the title Rabban (a title higher than a Rabbi, given only to presidents of the highest religious council) and like his grandfather, he was also given the title of Elder. His most well-known pupil was the apostle Paul (Acts 22:3). In Acts 5:34–39 Luke described him as a Pharisee and a teacher of the law honoured by the people and recorded that he interceded on behalf of the apostles when they were on trial before the Sanhedrin.

Like his grandfather, Hillel, Gamaliel was the originator of many lenient legal ordinances, in particular laws affecting women and non-Jews. Gamaliel's importance is reflected in the Talmud: "When Rabban Gamaliel the Elder died, regard for the Torah ceased, and purity and piety died."[5]

His son, Shimon ben Gamaliel, was one of the foremost leaders in the Jewish uprising against Rome (AD 66). His grandson, Gamaliel II, was the first president of the Sanhedrin after the destruction of the Second Temple in AD 70.

Roman Catholic and Eastern Orthodox tradition claim that he was converted and baptised by Peter and John, together with his younger son Abibon, and fellow teacher, Nicodemus, suggesting that he kept his conversion a secret so that he might continue to be a member of the Sanhedrin, covertly helping the Early Christians.

**John Mark** – John, also known as Mark, was the son of a wealthy woman named Mary who lived in Jerusalem (Acts 12:12).

---

4. Shabbat 15a.

5. Mishnah Sotah 9:15.

According to references in Philemon 24, Colossians 4:10, and 2 Timothy 4:11, he was the cousin of Barnabas. John accompanied Paul and Barnabas on their first missionary journey to Cyprus, but then left them in Perga and returned to Jerusalem. We do not know for certain what precipitated this departure, but it was of a sufficiently serious nature that Paul refused to take him along the second time. Barnabas took Mark with him to Cyprus. At some point, Paul was reconciled to both Barnabas (1 Corinthians 9:5–6) and John Mark (Colossians 4:10; Philemon 23; 2 Timothy 4:11). Quoting from Papias, Eusebius indicated that John Mark, in his capacity as Peter's student, scribe, or interpreter, wrote the Gospel of Mark.[6] According to tradition John Mark was the founder of the Church of Alexandria.[7]

**Elymas, Bar-Jesus** – It is possible that this man, the son of Joshua, was a Babylonian Jew who had acquired the skills and beliefs of the Persian Magi as the name Elymas appears to be a Greek transliteration of the Arabic word for Magus. As the proconsul is described as an "intelligent man" it is not surprising that he had a wise magician in his employ. He no doubt opposed Paul and Barnabas as he feared losing his position of authority.

**Sergius Paulus** – Lucius Sergius Paulus was a Proconsul under Emperor Claudius stationed in Paphos on the island of Cyprus. He was Paul's first recorded convert on the First Missionary Journey. Due to several inscriptions found in Rome, Cyprus, and Pisidian Antioch some scholars believe that it is possible that the proconsul's family were originally from Pisidian

---

6. Eusebius, the Ecclesiastical History, 3.39.

7. https://copticorthodoxanswers.org/st-mark-founder-of-coptic-church/.

Antioch and that this was the reason why Paul and Barnabas travelled there after leaving Cyprus.[8] It is also possible that Paul did not require that the proconsul be circumcised and that this caused a theological dispute between him and John Mark leading to the latter's early departure from the group.

**Simeon, Niger** – Other that being mentioned as one of the prophets and teachers in the church in Antioch in Acts 13:1 very little is known about Simon. It is possible that he was called Niger because he was of African descent.

**Lucius** – Lucius of Cyrene may have been one of the founding members of the church in Antioch (Acts 13:1). He was one member of the group who prayed and fasted and commissioned Barnabas and Saul to take the Gospel to Asia. Acts 11:19–20 may indicate that he was one of the men from Cyrene who went to Antioch and began a cross-cultural ministry to Greek speaking citizens. According to Orthodox Church tradition, he was appointed by John Mark to be the first bishop of Cyrene.[9]

**Manaen** the friend of Herod the Tetrarch – A teacher in the church at Antioch, Manaen is said to have been "brought up" with Herod Antipas. He was another member of the group that commissioned Paul and Barnabas. Together with Lucius and Niger, he was possibly one of the founding members of the church at Antioch. Manaen may have been a source for Luke who provided details about Herod Antipas and other members of the Herodian family (Luke 3:1, 19, 20; 8:3; 9:7–9; 13:31, 32; 23:8–12; Acts 12). It is possible that he was converted together with Joanna, the wife of Chuza, Herod's steward (Luke 8:3).

---

8. https://biblearchaeologyreport.com/2019/11/15/sergius-paulus-an-archaeological-biography/.

9. https://orthodoxwiki.org/Archdiocese_of_Cyrene.

**Timothy** – Timothy was the son of a Greek father and a Jewish mother. His mother and grandmother, Eunice and Lois, were apparently strong believers (2 Timothy 1:1–5) and had taught Timothy the Scriptures well. It is probable that Timothy first met Paul and Barnabas in Lystra on their first missionary journey. He joined Paul and Silas on the second missionary journey, after being circumcised by Paul to avoid future misunderstandings. It is likely that he was still very young at this time as later, in 1 Timothy 4:12, Paul exhorted Timothy not to let others look down upon him due to his youth. It is remarkable to think that this young man served a newly planted church in Thessalonica after Paul was forced to leave! Timothy served in several other churches (1 Corinthians 4:17; Philippians 2:19), as well as in Ephesus (1 Timothy 1:3) where he was apparently imprisoned and released (Hebrews 13:23) and later served as Bishop until he was clubbed to death by an angry mob in AD 97. He is mentioned in 2 Corinthians, Philippians, Colossians, 1 and 2 Thessalonians, and Philemon. Paul called him "my true son in the faith" (1 Timothy 1:2). It appears that Timothy had some form of chronic stomach illness (1 Timothy 5:23).

## Places mentioned

**Antioch** – The city was founded by Seleucus I Nicator and named after his father, Antiochus.[10] Situated at the foot of Mount Silpius, on the east bank of the Orontes River, and a day's journey inland from its port Seleucia Pieria, Antioch was strategically located at the juncture of several main trade routes. Many people groups, including Jews were settled there giving

---

10. "Although there were sixteen Antiochs in the ancient world – this and Pisidian Antioch are the only two mentioned in the Bible." Wilson, *Biblical Turkey: A Guide to the Jewish and Christian Sites of Asia Minor*, 62.

rise to a multiplicity of religions. Early Church tradition states that Peter established the churches in Antioch in AD 34.[11] In AD 45, many Jews migrated to Antioch during the persecution recorded in Acts 11. Barnabas and Saul were sent out from Antioch on the first missionary journey about AD 46.

**Tarsus** – Shrouded in myth and tradition, the founding of the city remains uncertain, but it was inhabited from about 3000 BC on. Although it was located 16 km from the Mediterranean coast it was connected to the sea by the Rhegma and Cydnus rivers. There was a sizeable Jewish population that had received Roman citizenship in the city of which Paul's family was part. Paul used Tarsus as a base for about 10–15 years after fleeing Jerusalem (Acts 9:30) planting churches in Cilicia.[12]

**Cyprus** – This is the third largest island in the Mediterranean, 222 km long, 97 km wide, with mountains reaching a height of 1007 m. Salamis is the eastern port city where Paul, Barnabas, and John Mark landed from Antioch. They would have travelled along the southern Roman road to the provincial capital, Paphos.[13]

**Perga** – Founded in 300 BC as a colony of Pergamum, Perga was situated 5 km west of the navigable Cestrus River and 10 km from the Mediterranean accessible by road to its port at Magydus. It was the terminus of the Via Sebaste and, as such, the gateway to the Anatolian plateau. It was the port of entry

---

11. Eusebius 3, 36. See also Origen's homilies on Luke VI, 4. Patrologia Graeca 13:1814 in https://en.wikipedia.org/wiki/Saint_Peter and http://ww1.antiochian.org/patofant. See also: https://christianity.stackexchange.com/questions/68875/is-there-any-evidence-to-support-the-claim-that-the-apostle-st-peter-founded-th.

12. Wilson, 120–23.

13. Wilson, 113.

for Paul, Barnabas, and John Mark. Paul and Barnabas returned to Perga on their way back to Antioch. Although no mention is made of a synagogue in the city, Jews were known to be present.[14]

**Pisidian Antioch** – Situated at 1236 m and strategically located on an east-west road that went from Ephesus to the Cilician Gates, Emperor Augustus used the city as a military base. It was linked to Perga by two roads, one of which was the Via Sebaste. While the central route was the most direct, it ascended precipitously through the steep Taurus Mountain gorges. Paul and Barnabas probably used the easier western route.[15]

**Iconium** – Iconium is one of the oldest occupied cities in the world. The Via Sebaste connected with the main southern highway here. It was linked with the Lycaonian cities of Lystra and Derbe.

**Lystra** – Located 35 km southwest of Iconium, the city was colonised by Augustus in 25 BC as a military colony. Timothy, a man of mixed heritage (Acts 16:1, 3), who became a disciple and co-worker of Paul, was raised here by his Jewish grandmother Lois and mother Eunice (2 Timothy 1:5).[16]

**Derbe** – Derbe was a frontier town, situated on the border of eastern Lycaonia about 30 km from the road that led from the Cilician Gates to Iconium. Paul and Barnabas ended their first missionary journey here, but Paul returned on his later trips (Acts 16:1; 18:23).[17]

---

14. Wilson, 93–94.
15. Wilson, 96, 102–9.
16. Wilson, 167–68.
17. Wilson, 151–54.

# Paul's First Missionary Journey

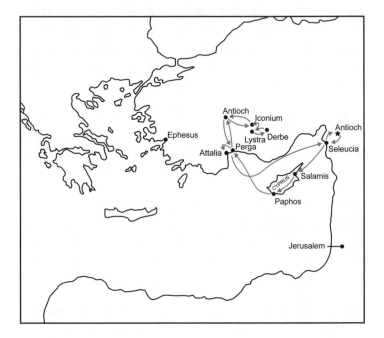

# Timeline

| | |
|---|---|
| AD 5? | Birth of Paul in Tarsus |
| AD 20? | Paul studies under Gamaliel II in Jerusalem |
| AD 33[1] | Crucifixion, Resurrection, Ascension, Pentecost |
| AD 33 | Jewish converts from different nations return home |
| AD 33–34 | Jerusalem, Judea, and Samaria: Stephen martyred, Philip's ministry |
| AD 34 | Paul converted and goes to Arabia for 3 years |
| AD 34 (tradition) | Peter establishes the church in Antioch |
| AD 37 | Paul returns to Damascus and escapes to Jerusalem |
| AD 37 | Herod Agrippa I appointed king |
| AD 37 | Paul with Peter |
| AD 37 | Paul to Tarsus |

---

1. For dating the crucifixion: https://www.bethlehemstar.com/the-day-of-the-cross/dating-the-crucifixion/ and https://www.bethlehemstar.com/the-day-of-the-cross/pilate-and-sejanus/.

| AD 38 | Peter heals Aeneas and Dorcas and brings the gospel to Cornelius |
| AD 39–42 (tradition) | Peter travels to Caesarea, Antioch, Pontus, Galatia, Cappadocia, Asia, and Bithynia, and on to Rome |
| AD 41 | Judea and Samaria were added to Herod Agrippa's realm |
| AD 42/43 | Barnabas goes to Antioch, summons Paul |
| AD 44 | Peter returns to Jerusalem via Pontus, Bithynia, Galatia, Cappadocia, and Antioch |
| AD 44 | The writing of 1 Peter |
| AD 44 | Barnabas and Paul in Jerusalem with gifts of food from Antioch |
| AD 44 | Execution of James, the brother of John; departure of the Twelve on international missions |
| AD 44 | Imprisonment and escape of Peter (to Caesarea, Antioch, Pontus, Galatia, Cappadocia, Asia, Bithynia, and on to Rome) |
| AD 44 | Death of Herod Agrippa I |
| AD 44–48 | Barnabas, Paul, and Mark to Antioch and then on their first missionary journey |
| AD 48 | Peter back to Jerusalem via Pontus, Bithynia, Galatia, Cappadocia, Asia, and Antioch |
| AD 48 | Peter and Paul's clash in Antioch |
| AD 48 | Galatians |

| AD 49 | Jerusalem Council |
| AD 49 | Jews expelled from Rome |
| AD 49 (biblical and tradition) | Paul and Silas to Macedonia and Athens, Barnabas and Mark to Cyprus, Luke meets Paul in Troas and then stays on in Philippi |
| AD 50–52 | Paul in Corinth; appears before Gallio, Proconsul of Achaia |
| AD 51–52 | 1 Thessalonians |
| AD 51–52 | 2 Thessalonians |
| AD 52–53 | Paul in Jerusalem and Antioch |
| AD 52–55 | Paul in Ephesus |
| AD 53/54 | 1 Corinthians |
| AD 54 | Nero becomes emperor |
| AD 55–56 | Paul through Macedonia, Illyricum, and western Greece |
| c. 55–56 | Philippians |
| c. 55–56 | Philemon |
| c. AD 55–56 | Colossians |
| c. AD 55–56 | Ephesians |
| AD 56 | 2 Corinthians |
| AD 57 | Paul in Corinth, Philippi, and Jerusalem |
| AD 57 | Romans, from Corinth |
| AD 57–59 | Paul imprisoned in Caesarea Maritima under Felix and Festus |

| AD 59 | Paul shipwrecked on route to Rome |
| AD 60 | Paul in Rome |
| AD 62?[2] | Paul to Spain |
| AD 62–64 | 1 Timothy and Titus |
| AD 62–64 | 2 Timothy |
| AD 62–64 | Titus |
| AD 62 | James, the brother of Jesus, executed |
| AD 64 | Fire in Rome |
| AD 64/65 | Paul executed |

---

2. There is a strong possibility that Paul was released from imprisonment in Rome after being under house arrest for two years, at which time he went to Spain as he had planned and was then rearrested during Nero's persecution. "Owing to envy, Paul also obtained the reward of patient endurance, after being seven times thrown into captivity, compelled to flee, and stoned. After preaching both in the east and west, he gained the illustrious reputation due to his faith, having taught righteousness to the whole world, and come to the extreme limit of the west, and suffered martyrdom under the prefects. Thus, was he removed from the world, and went into the holy place, having proved himself a striking example of patience." I Clement 5.5–7 (AD 96/97, just 30 years after Paul's beheading!)

". . . the journey of Paul, who from the city [Rome] proceeded to Spain." Muratorian Canon lines 38–39.

"And Paul entered into the apostleship a year after the assumption of Christ; and beginning at Jerusalem, he advanced as far as Illyricum, and Italy, and Spain, preaching the Gospel for five-and-thirty years. And in the time of Nero, he was beheaded at Rome, and was buried there." Hippolytus of Rome, Ante-Nicene Fathers 5.255.

"Two years then [Paul] passed bound, in Rome; then he was set free; then, having gone into Spain, he saw Jews also in like manner; and then he returned to Rome, where he was slain by Nero." John Chrysostom, *Homilies on the Epistle to the Hebrews*, Nicene and Post-Nicene Fathers 1.14.364.

# Annex

# "Faith of Christ"

The Greek word *pistis* (faith/faithfulness) has quite a wide semantic range. It can mean faith, faithfulness, belief, trust, loyalty, conviction, confidence, reliance, credibility, or fidelity depending on the context and usage in a particular text or discussion. It could indicate a person's trust or faith in someone or something or it could indicate the faithfulness, dependability, or trustworthiness of the person or thing being trusted. Paul pairs the word *pistis* with the genitive *Christou* eight times in Romans 3:22, 26; Galatians 2:16, 20, and 3:22; Ephesians 3:12, and Philippians 3:9.

Scholars differ as to how the combination ought to be understood or translated. There are at least four possible ways: the objective genitive or anthropological view (faith in Christ), the subjective genitive or the Christological view (the faithfulness of Christ), the genitive of quality (Christ-faith), and the multifaceted option that incorporates all the other possibilities. I have chosen the subjective genitive option in my translation of Paul's letter to the Galatians for various reasons. Paul appears to quote from the Septuagint, the ancient Greek version of the Old Testament, which renders Habakkuk 2:4b as *o de dikaios ek pisteōs mou zēsetai* (the righteous shall live by my faithfulness) where "my" seems to refer to "God" in 2:4a. In context, Habakkuk appears to indicate that the righteous remnant will be preserved because of God's faithfulness. If this is the case, then it may be that Paul believed that any response of faith in Christ was only possible because of the faithfulness of Christ. Indeed, in Galatians 3:23 faith appears to be something external revealed in Christ.

For a helpful discussion on this subject, see Matthew Easter's article "Faith of Christ," pages 301–5 in *Dictionary of Paul and his Letters*.

# Bibliography

Bandy, Alan S., *An Illustrated Guide to the Apostle Paul: His Life, Ministry, and Missionary Journeys*. Grand Rapids: Baker Books, 2021.

Barnett, Paul. *Jesus and the Rise of Early Christianity: A History of New Testament Times*. Downers Grove: InterVarsity Press, 1999.

Bijl, Johannes W. H. van der. *Breakfast on the Beach*. Carlisle: Langham Preaching Resources, 2021.

———. *For the Life of the World*. Carlisle: Langham Preaching Resources, 2022.

Bomar, David, ed. *Journeys of the Apostle Paul*. Bellingham: Lexham, 2019.

Bruce, F. F. *Paul: Apostle of the Heart Set Free*. Grand Rapids: Eerdmans, 1977.

Chalke, Steve. *The Lost Message of Paul*. London: SPCK, 2019.

Easter, Matthew C. "Faith of Christ" pages 301–5 in *Dictionary of Paul and his Letters*, 2nd Edition, General Editor, Scott McKnight. Downers Grove: InterVarsity Press, 2023.

Flemming, Dean. *Contextualization in the New Testament: Patterns for Theology and Mission*. Downers Grove: IVP Academic, 2005.

Gorman, Michael J. *Reading Paul*. Eugene: Cascade Books, 2008.

Harvey, John D. *Listening to the Text: Oral Patterning in Paul's Letters*. Grand Rapids: Baker Books, 1998.

Hays, Richard B. *Echoes of Scripture in the Letters of Paul*. New Haven: Yale University Press, 1989.

———. *The Letter to the Galatians*. New Interpreters Bible 11. Nashville: Abingdon, 2000.

Jeffers, James S. *The Greco-Roman World of the New Testament Era: Exploring the Background of Early Christianity*. Downers Grove: InterVarsity Press, 1999.

Koehler, Paul F. *Telling God's Stories with Power: Biblical Storytelling in Oral Cultures*. Pasadena: William Carey Library, 2010.

Longenecker, Richard N. *The Acts of the Apostles*. The Expositor's Bible Commentary, Volume 9. Grand Rapids: Zondervan, 1981.

Moo, Douglas J. *A Theology of Paul and His Letters*. Biblical Theology of the New Testament. Grand Rapids: Zondervan, 2021.

Nanos, Mark D. *Reading Paul within Judaism*. Vol. 1 of *Collected Essays of Mark D. Nanos*. Eugene: Cascade, 2017.

Philo. *The Works of Philo Judaeus*. Translated by Charles Duke Yonge. London: H. G. Bohn, 1854–1890. http://www.earlychristianwritings.com/yonge/index.html.

Rendall, Frederic. *The Epistle to the Galatians*. Vol. 3 of The Expositor's Greek Testament. Peabody: Hendrickson, 2002.

Schnabel, Eckhard J. *Early Christian Mission: Paul and the Early Church*. Downers Grove: InterVarsity Press, 2004.

Schreiner, Thomas R. *Interpreting the Pauline Epistles*. 2nd ed. Grand Rapids: Baker Academic, 2011.

Stewart, James S. *A Man in Christ: The Vital Elements of St. Paul's Religion*. Pantianos Classics, 1935.

Stott, John R. W. *The Message of Acts: The Spirit, the Church and the World*. The Bible Speaks Today. Downers Grove: InterVarsity Press, 1990.

Valdez, Erbey Galvan. *On the Shores of Perga: How John Mark's Departure from the First Pauline Missionary Journey Changed the Gentile World*. Bloomington: Westbow, 2020.

Walker, Peter. *In the Steps of Saint Paul: An Illustrated Guide to Paul's Journeys*. Oxford: Lion Hudson, 2011.

Wall, Robert W. *The Acts of the Apostles*. Vol. 10 of *The New Interpreter's Bible*. Nashville: Abingdon, 2002.

Wangerin, Walter Jr. *Paul: A Novel*. Grand Rapids: Zondervan, 2000.

Wilson, Mark. *Biblical Turkey: A Guide to the Jewish and Christian Sites of Asia Minor*. Istanbul: Yayinlari, 2020.

Wright, N. T. *Paul and the Faithfulness of God*. Parts I-IV. Minneapolis: Fortress Press, 2013.

———. *Paul for Everyone: Galatians and Thessalonians*. Louisville: Westminster John Knox, 2004.

———. *Paul: A Biography*. London: SPCK, 2018.

## Bibles Consulted

*Africa Study Bible*. Edited by John Jsu. Oasis International, 2016.

*The Greek New Testament*, 3rd edition. Edited by Kurt Aland, Matthew Black, Carlo M. Martini, Bruce M. Metzger, and Allen Wikgren. Stuttgart: United Bible Societies, 1983.

*The Interlinear Bible*. Edited by Jay P. Green. Grand Rapids: Baker Books, 1985.

*The Jerusalem Bible: Reader's Edition*. New York: Doubleday, 1968.

*JPS Hebrew-English Tanakh: The Traditional Hebrew Text and the New JPS Translation*. 2nd ed. Philadelphia: Jewish Publication Society, 2000.

*The Kingdom New Testament: A Contemporary Translation*. N. T. Wright. Grand Rapids: Zondervan, 2011.

*NIV Archaeological Study Bible*. Grand Rapids: Zondervan, 2005.

*NRSV Cultural Backgrounds Study Bible: Bringing to Life the Ancient World of Scripture.*Edited by Keener Walton. Grand Rapids: Zondervan, 2019.

*The Passion Translation*. Edited by Brian Simmons. BroadStreet Publishing Group, 2018.

*A Reader's Hebrew and Greek Bible*. Edited by Richard J. Goodrich, Albert J. Lukaszewski,Philip A. Brown, and Bryan W. Smith. Grand Rapids: Zondervan, 2008.

*The Septuagint with Apocrypha: Greek and English*. Sir Lancelot C. L. Brenton. Grand Rapids: Zondervan, 1851.

**Langham**
PARTNERSHIP

Langham Literature and its imprints are a ministry of Langham Partnership.

Langham Partnership is a global fellowship working in pursuit of the vision God entrusted to its founder John Stott –

> *to facilitate the growth of the church in maturity and Christ-likeness through raising the standards of biblical preaching and teaching.*

**Our vision** is to see churches in the Majority World equipped for mission and growing to maturity in Christ through the ministry of pastors and leaders who believe, teach and live by the word of God.

**Our mission** is to strengthen the ministry of the word of God through:
- nurturing national movements for biblical preaching
- fostering the creation and distribution of evangelical literature
- enhancing evangelical theological education

especially in countries where churches are under-resourced.

**Our ministry**

*Langham Preaching* partners with national leaders to nurture indigenous biblical preaching movements for pastors and lay preachers all around the world. With the support of a team of trainers from many countries, a multi-level programme of seminars provides practical training, and is followed by a programme for training local facilitators. Local preachers' groups and national and regional networks ensure continuity and ongoing development, seeking to build vigorous movements committed to Bible exposition.

*Langham Literature* provides Majority World preachers, scholars and seminary libraries with evangelical books and electronic resources through publishing and distribution, grants and discounts. The programme also fosters the creation of indigenous evangelical books in many languages, through writer's grants, strengthening local evangelical publishing houses, and investment in major regional literature projects, such as one volume Bible commentaries like *The Africa Bible Commentary* and *The South Asia Bible Commentary*.

*Langham Scholars* provides financial support for evangelical doctoral students from the Majority World so that, when they return home, they may train pastors and other Christian leaders with sound, biblical and theological teaching. This programme equips those who equip others. Langham Scholars also works in partnership with Majority World seminaries in strengthening evangelical theological education. A growing number of Langham Scholars study in high quality doctoral programmes in the Majority World itself. As well as teaching the next generation of pastors, graduated Langham Scholars exercise significant influence through their writing and leadership.

To learn more about Langham Partnership and the work we do visit **langham.org**